AFRICA
Customs, Cultures, Legends, and Lore

Written and Illustrated
by Gina Capaldi

Good Apple

To Mom and Cory. I love you.

My sincerest gratitude to senior editor Susan Eddy for all her support, integrity, and
professionalism; to marketing director Annye Camara for her enthusiasm;
to editor Alexandra Behr for her patience and editorial expertise;
to Lisa Ann Arcuri for her sensitive and lovely design; and
to Mr. Sam Sandt, Professor of Anthropology, who
generously gave his time to review this book.

Senior Editor: Susan Eddy

Editor: Alexandra Behr

Designer: Lisa Ann Arcuri

GOOD APPLE
A Division of Frank Schaffer Publications, Inc.
23740 Hawthorne Boulevard
Torrance, CA 90505-5927

ISBN 1-56417-895-1

5 6 7 8 9   01 00 99

Contents

Introduction

Africa is three times larger than the United States and has more than 1,000 cultures. Its history is ancient, complex, vivid, and sometimes tragic. African history is *our* history, too. Enslaved Africans sent to the British colonies helped shape American history and culture.

Who lived in Africa long ago? What were their lives like? What contact did they have with other parts of the world? What were their beliefs? What problems did they have to overcome? These are daunting questions of a people most Americans know little about.

In *Africa: Customs, Cultures, Legends, and Lore,* students will learn how the ideals, beliefs, and geographic surroundings of various African groups shaped their everyday customs. Hands-on individual and group projects are intended to expand students' understanding of each culture at a more insightful level than might be experienced from a purely textbook-based approach.

The activities in this book are intended to inspire a historical understanding of each culture. Because the spiritual beliefs of Africans are entwined with everyday customs, ceremonies and rituals become an important vehicle for exploring that history. We've tried to approach these issues with an attitude of respect and with the intention of communicating both the mystery and complexity of African traditions. We hope you'll do the same.

Suggestions for Using This Book

You can use the information and projects in this book as the main component of your world history or African curriculum or to supplement textbooks and materials you already use. The stories and projects provide practice in language arts, critical thinking, cooperative learning, math, and social studies skills.

In each chapter you'll find

- background information detailing the history, customs, and traditions of Africans in specific regions.
- a retelling of an African legend.
- reproducibles showing a traditional man and woman from specific groups, everyday artifacts, and dwellings that students can decorate by following the color code provided. Use these pages as coloring sheets or in one of the projects described on pages 6–7.
- step-by-step directions for group and individual projects based on African culture and history.

You also get

- a large, colorful map poster showing women and men of various African regions dressed in traditional garments, along with their dwellings and special tools used every day.
- a bibliography listing extra resources for you and your students, including children's literature, activity books, and both specific and general reference books.

How to Use This Book

Start by sharing the background information with students. Show them the figures for each group and discuss clothing styles and how they differed from one region to the next. Look at the everyday artifacts and dwellings and help students connect the way each object looks with its practical use. Discuss how the climate and landscape affected how different groups of Africans lived.

Distribute copies of the reproducibles to students. Share some of the following ideas by using the elements on the reproducibles, but also encourage student suggestions.

Basic Materials

- corrugated cardboard, foam board, or clean meatpacking trays
- posterboard or oak tag
- scissors
- tempera paints
- white glue
- silicone glue
- hole punch
- thread or string
- self-drying clay

Dioramas

1. Enlarge dwelling on a copier.
2. Glue dwelling onto posterboard and cut out, leaving a 1-inch (2.5-cm) flap at the bottom so it will stand upright. (Figure 1)

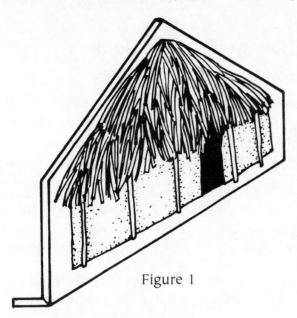

Figure 1

3. Mount dwelling on template; glue in place.
4. Repeat process with the costumed figures and tools.
5. Glue or tape figures into shoebox.

Other Tips:

- Use natural materials in your dioramas, such as leafy twigs for trees. These materials can also help you camouflage the tabs on the figures and artifacts.
- Make a kraal, or homestead, for your East or Southern African diorama. Roll self-drying clay into a long, thin coil. Wrap it around the base of the dwelling. Shove sticks into the clay to build a fence. (Figure 2)

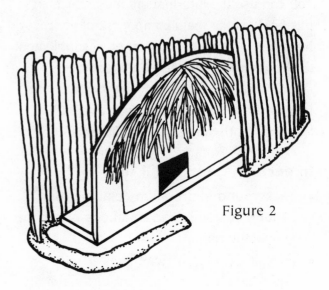

Figure 2

- Place samples of real or papier-mâché African foods next to individual dioramas. For example, position clay pots filled with squash or bananas near a West African diorama.
- Place miniature versions of some of the art projects next to individual dioramas, such as a small Berber rug (North Africa), gold spray-painted pebbles (West Africa), or small carved masks made of self-drying clay (central Africa).
- Use cardboard larger than the diorama to add painted backdrops or scenic triptychs of rain forest, rocky desert, or savanna scenes. Glue these scenes behind or around the dioramas. (Figure 3)

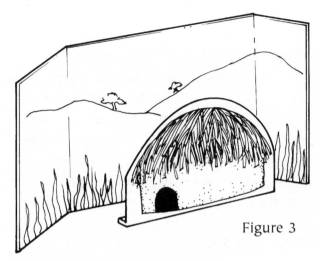

Figure 3

Three-dimensional Posters

1. Make posters detailing the geographic surroundings of African groups.
2. Enlarge dwellings, tools, and figures on a copier. Cut out and paint.
3. Trace enlarged shapes onto foam meatpacking trays or corrugated cardboard and cut out.
4. Mount figures and other objects onto the foam cutouts.
5. Attach objects to posters using silicone glue. (Figure 4)

(Note: The thicker the foam or cardboard, the more three-dimensional your posters will appear.)

Map Dioramas

1. Locate a map of Africa in an atlas. Draw the map on a large sheet of heavy cardboard or use an overhead projector to trace it.
2. Mix saturated papier-mâché and white glue. Use the mixture to add textures to the map. Paint regions or topographical features, using an atlas as a guide.
3. Enlarge regional dwellings, tools, artifacts, and African figures on a copier. Glue each item on white posterboard, leaving a 1-inch (2.5-cm) flap at the bottom so it will stand upright. Cut out.
4. Mount forms upright in their region onto the map. Glue in place. (Figure 5)

Figure 5

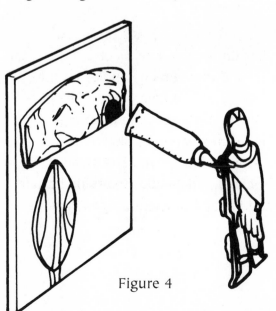

Figure 4

Mobiles

1. Enlarge dwellings on a copier and cut out. Mount onto lightweight posterboard.
2. Copy, cut out, and mount figures onto separate posterboard. Overlap figures onto dwellings and glue in place. (Figure 6)

Figure 6

3. Punch small holes at even intervals along the bottom edges of dwellings.
4. Mount tools and artifacts onto posterboard. Cut out. Punch holes along the top edges of each tool or artifact.
5. Thread tools and artifacts with lightweight string, thread, or fishing line. Tie onto dwellings so they hang freely.

Kwanzaa Celebration

The African American holiday of Kwanzaa is celebrated from December 26 to January 1. Participants honor African heritage, families, and cultural values. During Kwanzaa family members read and share inspiring stories about famous and ordinary African Americans from the past and present. Kwanzaa is based on seven principles: unity, self-determination, collective work and responsibility, cooperative economics, purpose, creativity, and faith. The Kwanzaa rituals help people affirm the principles to their lives.

Before You Begin

1. Kwanzaa has symbolic items representing the seven days of the holiday and its seven principles.

Materials

- 1 black candle
- 3 red candles
- 3 green candles
- candleholder for 7 candles
- handmade mat
- large cup
- bowl of fruit
- ears of corn for each student
- handmade gifts (choose from the projects in this book)

2. In the candleholder, place three red candles on the left, one black candle in the center, and three green candles on the right. Place all the items except the gifts onto the mat. Discuss the meanings behind each symbol, as shown in parentheses: black candle (African Americans); red candles (working hard for a good life and freedom); green candles

(hope); handmade mat (handmade African crafts); large cup (unity among African Americans); bowl of fruit (reward for hard work); ears of corn (hope for the future).

3. Make a poster with the seven principles, or *Nguzo Saba,* to display in your class. Discuss how the symbolism of the Kwanzaa items corresponds to the principles.

Kwanzaa Principles (*Nguzo Saba*)

1. Unity (Umoja): Togetherness in the family, the community, and the world

2. Self-determination (Kujichagulia): The ability to decide your own future

3. Collective Work and Responsibility (Ujima): To work and be responsible for each other as a group

4. Cooperative Economics (Ujamaa): To operate shops and businesses; to learn skills at school that can help you become a successful business owner

5. Purpose (Nia): To do what you can to improve yourself and your people

6. Creativity (Kuumba): To make your community beautiful and strong

7. Faith (Imani): To believe in yourself and your culture

How to Celebrate Kwanzaa

4. On the first day, light the black candle and discuss the first principle. Ask students how they can apply it to their daily lives. Share stories about famous African Americans and how they influenced American culture and the world. Also read aloud stories about ordinary African Americans who lead generous lives.

5. On the second day, light the black candle and use it to light the first red candle on the left. Discuss with students the second principle and why it is important. On the third day, light the first green candle on the right, and use it to light the candles from the previous two days. Discuss the importance of the third principle. Follow this process each day until all the candles are lit.

6. On the seventh day, invite students to distribute their handmade gifts to friends or to classmates whose names were chosen at random.

Kwanzaa Information Center

http://www.melanet.com/kwanzaa/

People of West Africa

Background Information

Some of the West African countries that border the Atlantic Ocean are Gambia, Guinea-Bissau, Guinea, Sierra Leone, Liberia, Côte d'Ivoire, Ghana, Togo, Benin, Nigeria, and Cameroon. Much of this area is covered by tropical rain forests.

Senegal and parts of Mauritania also border the Atlantic, but the land shifts from savannas to shrublands to the Sahara. The landscape of the inland countries of Mali, Burkina Faso, and Niger ranges from savannas to desert.

At one time, some of the major groups were the **Hausa, Yoruba, Fulani,** and **Ashanti.** West Africans have survived the domination of powerful ancient kingdoms, Middle Eastern invasions, European conquests, and the debilitating slave trade. Their customs and beliefs are hundreds of years old.

Early Migrations and Daily Life

West Africans originated from the late–Stone Age people of the Sahara. The Sahara was once lush and tropical. The first inhabitants lived in hundreds of scattered villages along riverbanks. As the region slowly dried up, groups migrated into more inhabitable land.

It is believed that about 4,000 years ago many groups ventured further south into tropical rain forests. They ate yams, millet, wild grains, onions, roots, kola nuts, watermelons, snails, and fish. Cassava from South America was introduced in the fifteenth century. In the drier sub-Saharan climates, people owned goats and cattle. However, domesticated animals were not kept in the rain forest because disease-breeding insects would infect and kill the herds.

West Africa was rich in minerals. Some records indicate that gold was so prevalent that it could be found lying in streams. People collected gemstones, mined for copper and gold, and harvested rock salt from dry riverbeds. Everyone was allowed to mine for gold, but a certain amount was given to the king.

Mali Carved Mask

FACT

Salt was such a valuable commodity that it was traded pound for pound for gold.

As with many rich kingdoms, owning slaves was commonplace. Before the arrival of Europeans, West Africans were accosted and forced into slavery only during intertribal wars. Often, owners would marry their enslaved captives.

Customs and Beliefs

West Africans relied on large extended families for child rearing and survival. The Ashanti built family compounds throughout their villages. A wealthy man might have two or more wives living in separate huts. Both parents helped raise their children. Children learned to behave in public, honor their elders, and respect each other's property. At the age of eight, boys were sent to their fathers' huts for further training and instruction. Girls remained with their mothers and were taught to farm, keep house, and cook.

In the ninth century, Arab traders introduced Islam to West Africans. West Africans were initially opposed to this religion, but Muslim trader-clerics were vigilant in claiming converts. Some West African kings accepted this new religion for political purposes, thus opening the door to influence local populations.

Ancient Kingdoms of the Savanna

Gold was the major commodity in West African history. It was traded with North Africans for salt as early as 500 B.C. Much of the gold used during the Roman Empire, Middle Ages, and Renaissance came from West Africa. During the seventh century A.D., Arab traders became the major controllers of the gold-salt trade. Their relationship with West Africa lasted more than 1,000 years.

Due to the wealth of this region, several ancient kingdoms emerged. Three early classical kingdoms were Ghana, Mali, and Songhai. The Kingdom of Ghana first arose around A.D. 700. During this time, Timbuktu developed into a major economic port for the gold–salt trade and became the center of religion, culture, and education. A mosque was built to train Muslim clerics, and scholars studied philosophy, medicine, and mathematics.

FACT

Ancient Ashanti kings wore gold castanets on their fingers and used them to silence their courts.

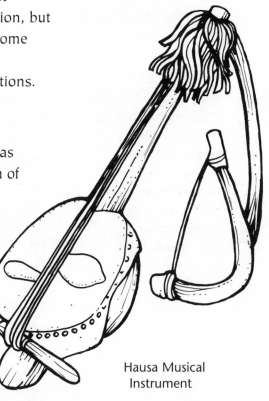

Hausa Musical Instrument

Ivory Tusk
Horn

The Kingdom of Ghana was absorbed into the Kingdom of Mali in A.D. 1200. This new kingdom had great political power. It became a major trading empire whose territories reached farther west than its predecessor.

Songhai, the greatest kingdom of classical West Africa, emerged in A.D. 1350. This kingdom slowly usurped the territory of Mali. It grew so large that its soldiers could not patrol the outer regions. Moroccans, who were searching for secret gold mines, attacked outlying villages. The Songhai army's spears and arrows could not match the Moroccans' cannons and guns. Songhai fell under Moroccan power in A.D. 1590.

Arrival of Europeans

Portuguese sailors first landed on the west coast of Africa in A.D. 1470. Aware of its gold reserves, they sought to establish direct trade with the West Africans. The Portuguese built a fort called El Mina after finding the Ashanti gold mines. El Mina held goods and gold received in trade. The Portuguese and the Ashanti pursued trade with each other and became wealthy. West Africans were influenced by Portuguese missionaries, machinery, guns, and new foods.

FACT

"Talking" drums were used to broadcast news throughout the territory. Everyone understood the language of the drums.

The Spanish sugar plantations in the Caribbean and in Mexico required imported labor. By the 1700s, slave trafficking was rampant. The British, Spaniards, Danes, and French came to West Africa in pursuit of gold, ivory, and slaves. In 1791, Great Britain outlawed the slave trade and in 1820 it abolished slavery.

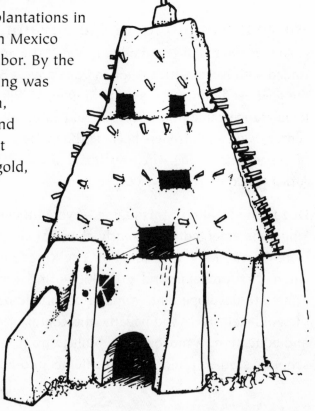

Fourteenth-Century Sankore
Mosque at Timbuktu

Searching for Gold
(Ashanti)

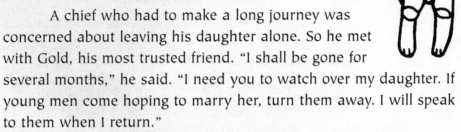

A chief who had to make a long journey was concerned about leaving his daughter alone. So he met with Gold, his most trusted friend. "I shall be gone for several months," he said. "I need you to watch over my daughter. If young men come hoping to marry her, turn them away. I will speak to them when I return."

"I will look after your daughter as if she were my own," Gold replied.

The chief felt confident that his daughter was safe and went off on his journey. Many months passed and he did not return. Young men came seeking the young girl's hand in marriage, but Gold turned them away. However, he became very worried that something terrible had happened to the chief. When another young man asked for the chief's daughter's hand, Gold agreed, saying, "Since I am watching over her, you must make the marriage settlement with me." Gold received great riches in exchange for the young girl.

A while later, Gold heard that the chief was on his way home. He was terrified. "How will I ever be able to face my friend?" he wondered. Gold grabbed everything he owned and moved to the grasslands.

When the chief returned, he asked, "Where are Gold and my daughter?" The people replied, "Gold has fled," and they told him about his daughter's marriage. The chief was furious! "You must bring Gold back," he declared. "But where will we look?" the people asked. "Everywhere," he said. "I will not rest until I see him."

So the people searched as they hunted food. They searched as they dug yams. Every trader that passed through was asked, "Have you seen Gold?" But no one knew where Gold was hiding. The search still goes on. And that is why, even today, the people are still looking for Gold.

Group Project

Brass Proverb Wall Hanging (Ashanti)

The Ashanti made beautiful items out of gold and brass. Gold was one of their earliest forms of currency. The Ashanti weighed gold dust for trade by creating brass counterweights. Each weight had a special saying or proverb attached to it.

Before You Begin

Distribute and discuss the Proverb Designs page. Ask students if they recognize any of them. Discuss how the designs illustrate the proverbs. For instance, the strutting rooster helps explain the proverb "Don't be so proud, your mother was a mere eggshell." Some students may wish to create designs for other proverbs, special sayings, or historical events.

Materials (for each student)

- oak tag, 5 x 7 inches (12.5 x 17.5 cm)
- brass-colored spray paint
- tube of clear or white caulking
- hole punch
- 3 brass rings
- drawing paper
- carbon paper
- wooden dowel, 1/4 inch x 6 inches (.5 x 15 cm)

To Make Proverb Designs

1. Select an Ashanti proverb design or choose another proverb and create a corresponding design on drawing paper.

2. If necessary, enlarge design on a copier to fit vertically on oak tag.

3. Slip carbon paper between design and oak tag. Tape in place. (Figure 1)

Figure 1

4. Trace design onto oak tag with a dried-up ballpoint pen or dull pencil. Remove design and carbon paper. Make sure lines are visible.

5. Following the design, squeeze caulking onto oak tag. Let dry. (Figure 2)

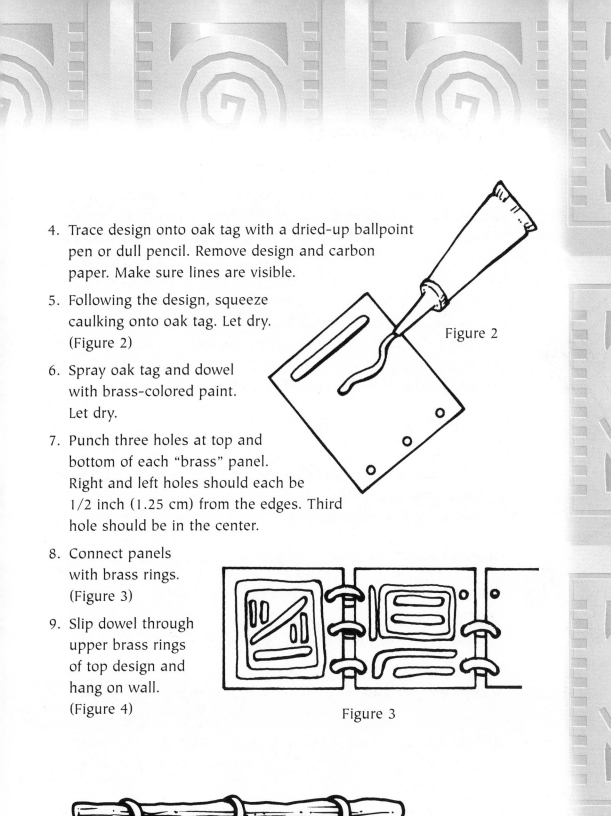

Figure 2

6. Spray oak tag and dowel with brass-colored paint. Let dry.

7. Punch three holes at top and bottom of each "brass" panel. Right and left holes should each be 1/2 inch (1.25 cm) from the edges. Third hole should be in the center.

8. Connect panels with brass rings. (Figure 3)

9. Slip dowel through upper brass rings of top design and hang on wall. (Figure 4)

Figure 3

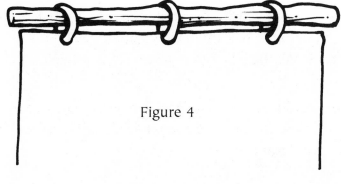

Figure 4

Individual Project

Casting Brass Weights (Ashanti)

Most of the Ashanti weights were cast in brass through the lost wax process. First an Ashanti master carver fashioned a figure or design in beeswax. Then he encased the wax in clay, poked a small hole in the clay, and let it dry. He then placed the clay casing into the fire, where the wax would melt and seep out through the hole. Afterward the artisan poured molten brass into the cavity where the wax once was. When the metal hardened, he broke the clay mold, then removed and polished the brass design. Students will learn how to cast a mold using a very simple process similar to the lost wax process. *There is no firing or use of dangerous metals in this project.*

Figure 1

Materials (for each student)

– Plastina or non-drying clay
– small cardboard jewelry box, about 2 x 3 1/2 inches (5 x 8.75 cm)
– plaster of Paris, 1/8 cup (30 ml)
– brass-colored spray paint

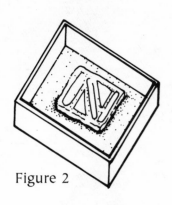

Figure 2

To Make the Figure

1. Select a simple geometric design from the Proverb Designs page.

2. Flatten a piece of clay to make a 1-x-1-x-1/4 inch (2.5-x-2.5-x-.5 cm) square. With pins, pencils, or other utensils, carve the design into the clay. (Figure 1)

3. Press another wad of clay into the bottom of the box. Spread until the clay is 1/2-inch (1.25-cm) thick. (Figure 2)

4. Place the carved design carefully in the center of the box. Use more clay to build a 1/4-inch- (.5-cm-) tall frame around the design. (Figure 3)

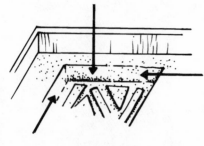

Figure 3

5. Mix the plaster of Paris with water until it has the consistency of pudding. Pour it onto the design, making sure it does not spill over the gutter. Shake the box lightly to get rid of any air bubbles. Let dry.

6. Break apart the cardboard box and peel away the clay. Use a straight pin to flick away any clay stuck to the plaster. Spray the plaster weight with brass-colored paint.

16

People of West Africa

Proverb Designs (Ashanti)

 Proverb: One who follows the elephant will never get wet from the dew of bushes. (Follow an important man and he will always protect you.)

 Proverb: Bark will always fall to the ground if there is no one to help you pick it up. (Accept help when you need it.)

Proverb: Don't rub the back of a porcupine. (Don't risk getting involved with those who can hurt you.)

Proverb: No one lives forever, but their accomplishments do.

Proverb: No one can survive without a good leader.

 Proverb: Birds that are the same kind stick together.

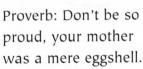 Proverb: Don't be so proud, your mother was a mere eggshell.

Proverb: Even if the elephant's tail is too short, it still whisks away flies. (Handicaps and disadvantages are no excuse for not trying.)

People of West Africa

Garments to Color (Ashanti)

Color the traditional garments by following the key below.

Woman's
Kente Cloth

Man's
Kente Cloth

Color Key

a. Yellow
b. Purple
c. Orange
d. Green
e. Brown

(Teacher's note: Use this page as a flat coloring sheet or enlarge each item to use in one of the special projects described on pages 6-7.)

18

People of West Africa

Tools and Dwellings to Color (Ashanti)

Color each item by using the key below.

Carved Mask

Umbrella

Hardwood Ladle

Fertility Doll

Brush Hut

Gold Knife

Pottery

Color Key

a. Yellow
b. Gold
c. Brown
d. Red
e. Green
f. Tan
g. Purple

Talking Drum

(Teacher's note: Use this page as a flat coloring sheet or enlarge each item to use in one of the special projects described on pages 6–7.)

People of Central Africa

Background Information

Central Africa encompasses the countries of Equatorial Guinea, Gabon, Congo, northern Angola, Central African Republic, Zaire, and western Uganda. Much of this region is covered by tropical rain forests so dense that the inhabitants were cut off from the rest of the continent.

At one time, some of the major groups were the **Azande, Fiote, Bambala, Bakongo,** and **Pygmies.** Because of their isolation, they developed beliefs and lifestyles different from those in other areas. This is particularly evident in the Congo basin, which was mostly uncharted until the twentieth century.

Daily Life

The Pygmies lived in the heart of the Congo basin. Anthropologists believe the Pygmies have inhabited the rain forest since around 5000 B.C. The Pygmies, or Bambuti, averaged from four to five feet in height. They made their homes out of trees or poles and very big leaves. The forest provided an abundance of roots, nuts, bananas, and other fruit.

The Pygmies were excellent hunters and could ward off aggressive intruders. Their small statures allowed for easier movement through the thick rain forest. Animals were killed with poison darts or trapped in vine nets.

Around 2000 B.C., Bantu-speaking groups and others migrated south from what is now Cameroon in West Africa. Many settled in villages along the shores of the Congo River or moved into the savannas outside the rain forest. They cultivated crops and raised livestock.

Other Bantu migrations took place in around 500 B.C., into what is now Zaire and northern Angola. They also raised livestock, fished, and cultivated the land. They learned how to smelt iron and copper into weapons and tools. They wove

Wooden Cow Masks of Eastern Congo

FACT

Pygmy children played with balls made of raw latex from rubber trees, which were introduced to Africa from South America in the sixteenth century.

beautiful fabrics from the fibers of raffia palm trees, which they traded for other goods.

The Bantu and Pygmy groups relied on each other. Trading was usually cloaked in darkness, because the Pygmies were wary of strangers. A Bantu-speaking group such as the Bakongo would leave items in the open fields. Later, Pygmy hunters would stealthily leave the forest and replace the items with their goods.

Customs and Beliefs

The Pygmies believed that all good came from the rain forest and that no harm would come to them if they stayed within it. The Bantu believed that dangerous spirits possessed the dark rain forest and rarely ventured in.

Few people were as prolific at creating masks and statues as those who lived near the western coast of the rain forest region. These religious items were used for initiation rites into adulthood, preparations for war, and death ceremonies. The terrifying expressions on the masks often represented supernatural forces. Wearers of masks believed they were possessed by spirits. They often went into deep trances, dancing to ceremonial music for hours.

Kingdoms of the Congo River

In around the fifth century A.D., small kingdoms and chiefdoms emerged along the mouth of the Congo, or Zaire, River. The kings, royal courts, and officials oversaw effective systems of law and order. Warfare and clashes, though still common, became more symbolic. For instance, opposing groups might brandish spears or take prisoners to be ransomed for cattle.

Between the fifteenth and eighteenth centuries, other kingdoms, such as the Luba, Lunda, and Malawi, emerged in the northern and southern parts of central Africa. These kingdoms benefited from trade with the Swahilis and Arabs.

FACT

Laws and customs were strictly followed in central Africa. Accused persons were brought to trial before an official of the court. They had to prove their innocence by explaining their point of view. They tried to justify their case by stating moral principles from common proverbs, sayings, or songs.

FACT

Oranges, lemons, and bananas are indigenous to central Africa.

Woman With Lip Disk. It is believed that this custom originated as a part of an initiation into womanhood or was used as a device to discourage Arab enslavement.

Ivory, slaves, and gold were always important trading commodities between the eastern traders and central groups. In the nineteenth century there was such a great demand that the Swahili and Arab traders used unscrupulous means to get what they wanted, with little resistance from central groups. Congo law stated that slaves could be taken only during a war. To acquire slaves, Arab traders pitted one African group against the other and caused much mistrust among people. Wars, which were once casual, became more aggressive and continual.

Arrival of Europeans

Helmet Mask
From Zaire

The Portuguese first encountered the Kongo Kingdom in 1482. In 1491, King Joao I, the Mani Kongo, entered into a friendly trade agreement with the Portuguese. Kongo nobles wanted to expand their chiefdoms, develop their technology and military strength, and become literate. In exchange the Portuguese planned to enrich their colony with gold, copper, and other goods. They also wanted to claim new territories, expand missionary work, and acquire enslaved workers for Brazilian sugar plantations.

King Joao I allowed his people to be converted to Catholicism. He was baptized and took a Christian name. He sent ambassadors to Portugal to represent him and his people.

The growing friendship and peaceful trade between the Portuguese and central Africans led to grim results. By 1526 the Portuguese had extracted so many slaves that the area became underpopulated. King Alfonso, the Mani Kongo at that time, sent a letter to the Portuguese king requesting that the slave trade end. He feared that his people would disappear. He received no response, and the slaving continued until the 1800s.

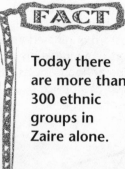

The Father-in-Law Below the Earth (Bakongo)

One day a man found some pigs that had eaten his crop of bananas. Furious, the man chased away the pigs and managed to wound one on its tail. The man was determined to find the pigs' owner so he could demand payment.

He gathered both good and damaged bananas and followed the pigs' trail to the edge of a pond. Without thinking, he jumped into the water. To his surprise there was a village at the pond's depths. Greeting the chief, he said, "Are you the owner of the pigs who destroyed my crops? If you are, I have come for payment of the fruit your pigs destroyed."

The wise chief ate a piece of the fruit. "I have never tasted anything so wonderful," he said. "I will give you more than a regular payment; I will allow you to marry my beautiful daughter." The man happily agreed. As the man and his new wife prepared to leave the village for the world above, the chief warned, "You may never visit us during the dry season. Only come here during the rainy season."

The couple were happy for a year, and in that time they had a healthy child. But one day the woman started screaming. She cried to her husband, "Our baby is deathly ill. Please let me take him to see my father, because he has great magic. Only he can save our son!"

"It is impossible, my wife," the man said. "Your father forbade us to visit during the dry season." She continued to plead until her husband gave in. At the pond, the family sunk into its depths. Instead of a thriving village, they found all the plants, trees, and people dead. The woman and her son died, too. The man ran to escape but could not find an opening out of the pond.

Suddenly a drop of rain fell. Then more and more until the land was drenched. Everything came back to life. The man followed the sounds of chattering villagers. There he found his wife and son alive. Indeed, there is magic with the rain.

Group Project

Central African Ceremonial Masks

Central African woodcarvers were highly skilled at their craft. They also had much respect toward all living things. The woodcarver believed that carving the wood caused it pain. Before he started, he would ask the spirit of the tree for forgiveness.

Before You Begin

- Distribute and discuss the Mask Designs page. Invite students to name the emotion each expression might represent. Encourage students to design faces with exaggerated expressions to incorporate into their masks.
- Help students make connections between the belief in tree spirits and the importance of trees to a central African's daily life. Describe ways that a tree provides food and shelter to many living things. Ask students to tell how people today can protect trees and forests.

Materials (for each student)

- flour, 1 cup (240 ml)
- salt, 1 cup (240 ml)
- water
- aluminum foil
- plastic knife
- tempera paints: white, red, black
- raffia or dried grass
- white glue
- small shells (optional)

To Make a Mask

1. Choose a mask from the Mask Designs page or create another design.

2. Mix flour and salt. Slowly add water until mixture can be rolled into a ball. Add extra salt and flour if the mixture is sticky.

Figure 1

3. Lay dough on aluminum foil and flatten into a 1/2-inch- (1.25-cm-) thick oval. (Figure 1)

4. Cut designs into the form with a plastic knife. Add bits of the clay to build protrusions such as eyes or noses (Figure 2). Air-drying takes one week. If baking masks, set oven at 250° and cook for 1 to 1 1/2 hours. To check for dryness, press hard into thicker areas.

Figure 2

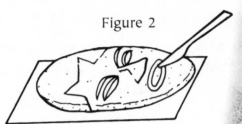

5. Paint the mask with a white base coat. Use other colors as accents. Do not add too much water to the paints, as they will disintegrate the hardened dough. Allow paint to dry.

6. Gather raffia and dried grasses together. Trim across the top. (Figure 3)

7. Glue raffia in patches onto the mask, making a collar or beard up to the ear area. (Figure 4)

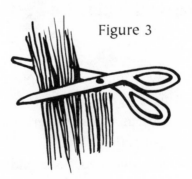
Figure 3

8. Glue shells or other natural objects on the mask.

Figure 4

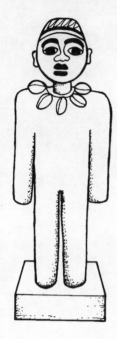

Individual Project

Papier-mâché Statues (Bakongo)

Central Africans created numerous types of statues. Many represented a person's ancestor, while others were fetishes. To use a fetish, a person would first awaken the spirit of the wood by driving a nail into the statue. Once a person had the spirit's attention, she or he would ask for a special favor. A woman might ask for an easy childbirth, whereas a man might request success in hunting.

Materials (for each student)

- plastic foam ball, 3 inches (7.5 cm), for the head
- plastic foam square, 1 x 1 inch (2.5 x 2.5 cm), for the neck
- plastic foam rectangle, 4 x 3 x 1 1/2 inches (10 x 7.5 x 3.75 cm), for the trunk
- 4 plastic foam cylinders 1 inch (2.5 cm) in diameter and 6 inches (15 cm) in length, for the arms and legs
- 1 plastic foam square, 6 x 6 x 1 1/2 inches (15 x 15 x 3.75 cm), for the base
- 10 large sheets of newspaper   - wooden toothpicks
- 1 cup (240 ml) white glue   - paint, mahogany or dark brown

Optional Materials

- small shells   - nails

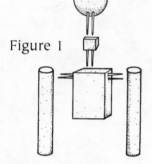

Figure 1

Figure 2

1. Rip newsprint into small pieces. Place in basin with water. Soak overnight to make pulp.
2. Squeeze out excess water and mix in glue. Knead to make papier-mâché.
3. Connect foam head, neck, and trunk with toothpicks and glue. Follow same process to add foam legs and arms. Let dry. (Figure 1)
4. Cover all plastic foam pieces with papier-mâché. (Figure 2)
5. Wet hands with water. Add more papier-mâché to define body. Let dry. (Figure 3)
6. Paint dark brown or mahogany. To make sculpture more authentic, embellish with small shells or press large steel nails into it.

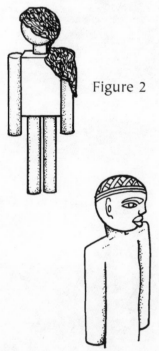

Figure 3

People of Central Africa

Mask Designs (Bakongo)

Bakongo carvers were noted for their distinctive masks. The masks often had expressive features, such as flat noses and teeth.

People of Central Africa

Garments to Color

Color the traditional garments by following
the key below.

Color Key

a. Dark Brown
b. Tan
c. White
d. Red
e. Gold
f. Orange

(Teacher's note: Use this page as a flat coloring sheet or enlarge each item to use in one of the special
projects described on pages 6-7.)

People of Central Africa

Tools and Dwellings to Color (Bakongo)

Color each item by following the color key below.

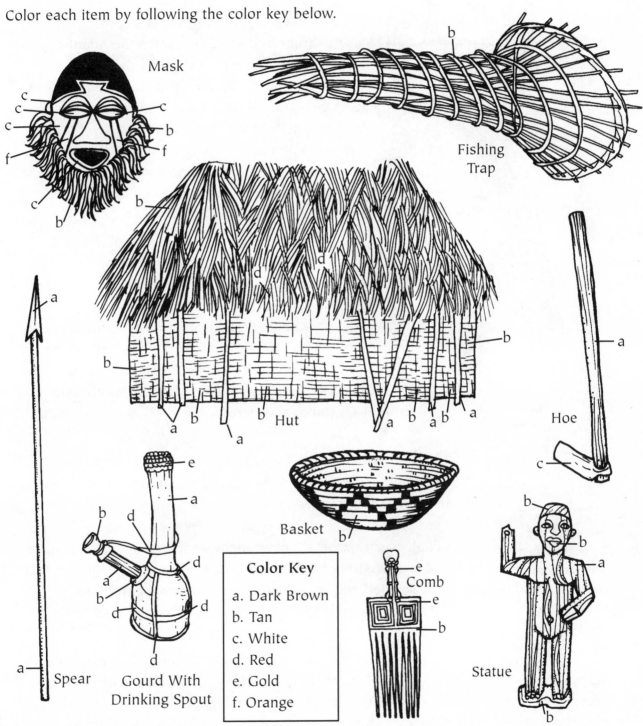

Mask

Fishing Trap

Hut

Spear

Gourd With Drinking Spout

Basket

Comb

Hoe

Statue

Color Key

a. Dark Brown
b. Tan
c. White
d. Red
e. Gold
f. Orange

(Teacher's note: Use this page as a flat coloring sheet or enlarge each item to use in one of the special projects described on pages 6-7.)

Herero
Headdress

People of Southwest Africa

Background Information

The southwest region of Africa is a sparse land of desert shrubs and sand dunes. On the Atlantic Coast lies the Namib Desert, which runs the length of Namibia (formerly Southwest Africa) and part of the Angola coastline. Further inland is the Kalahari Desert. Few people lived in these areas because of the severe weather and unappealing terrain. However, toward the northern fringes of Angola, wooded savannas abound and a kingdom once flourished.

A few **San** still live in the Kalahari Desert. They are perhaps Africa's oldest inhabitants. Their lifestyle is similar to those of their Stone Age ancestors, although they have used steel tools for hundreds of years. People such as the **Khoikhoi** and **Damara** moved from what is now South Africa to the southwest region during the 1600s. The major groups of what is now Angola were the **Ndongo**, **Ovimbundu**, **Ovambo**, and **Herero**.

Daily Life

Through the centuries the San developed unique ways to live off the land. They traveled in small bands in search of food. Hunters used poison arrows to kill big-game animals such as wildebeests, buffaloes, and zebras. They caught smaller animals with snares and leather string bags. The San dug up roots with digging sticks, then scraped and squeezed them to extract a bitter juice. Termites, caterpillars, grasshoppers, and ostrich eggs were also part of the San diet, as were watermelons.

Because water was scarce, finding and storing it became a daily chore. The San collected ostrich eggs, filled them with pond water, then capped them with dry-grass stoppers. They stuck hollow elephant grass in a hole, then sucked up groundwater and dribbled it out into an ostrich-egg container. Cleansing the body was often done by smearing grease over the body then dusting with powder.

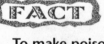

FACT

To make poison arrows, San hunters mixed the venom of puff adders, the crushed bodies of trapdoor spiders, and vegetable juices.

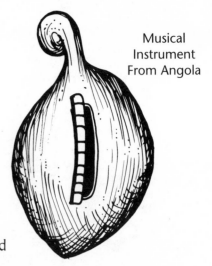

Musical Instrument From Angola

Groups owned territorial rights to hunting grounds, watering holes, and bee hives. These rights were collective. If caught, non-related trespassers on these lands might lose their lives.

The Herero claim to have entered the southwest region around the sixteenth century. They are closely related to southern Zulu groups. Like the Khoikhoi and Ovambo, the Herero were cattle and sheep herders. Women milked the cows and gathered wild roots and bulbs, and men watched over the herds.

The Ovimbundo and Ndongo lived closer to the savannas. The rich soil in that region supported crops of sorghum, nuts, and later, cassava.

Customs and Beliefs

The San believed that one great spirit, named Gaua, united the universe. He commanded the earth and sky, caused the sun to rise and set, and gave souls to newborns. Gaua created the first woman and man, from which every creature has sprung. Thus, the San believed that all creatures were their brothers.

FACT

The San found a plant whose scent kept lions away.

For the San, hunting depended more on good luck than on skill. Men wore charms or cut marks in their bodies to help ensure their success. Many of these incisions were made at the start of a boy's hunting career.

For most of the southwest Africans, dancing was more than a social activity. Many dances were connected with hunting, while others were used as a means to connect with their souls.

The Herero, Khoikhoi, and Ovambo believed that fire was sacred. Fires were erected on altars and lined with bones from sacrificed cattle. A guard would stand watch over the fire. If the fire went out, it symbolized disaster. Cattle were equally sacred, as was their milk, therefore the washing of cattle-related utensils was prohibited.

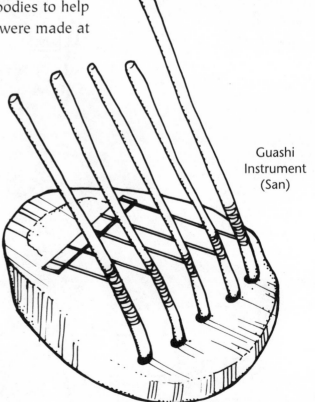

Guashi Instrument (San)

Ovimbundo Wooden Staff

Arrival of Europeans

In 1484 the Portuguese made a brief appearance off the coast of southwest Africa. The sand dunes and small bands of people living here offered little to the Portuguese, who were searching for trading goods and for people to enslave. The Portuguese left the coast to go further south. For the next few centuries this region remained free of European conflict or expansion.

In 1652, thirty Dutch settlers moved from what is now the country of South Africa to lands owned by the Khoikhoi. The Dutch seized the best pasture for themselves and pushed the Khoikhoi onto inferior land. A great rebellion ensued, but the Khoikhoi weapons were no match for the Dutch guns. The Khoikhoi who were not enslaved or killed retreated further into the Kalahari Desert.

During the nineteenth century, the Khoikhoi and Herero were in constant turmoil with each other. Both competed for European trade in exchange for guns and other items. The Dutch took advantage of the rivalry and pitted one group against the other, offering protection in exchange for land.

In 1908, diamonds were found on the surface of the Namib Desert, and later they were found on the beaches of Namibia. What was once considered a wasteland with sparse grazing land became known as a region with an unlimited supply of valuable gemstones. Today, many miners are migrant workers who must leave their tribal land for years at a time. The women stay at home to care for their families and cattle.

House With Painted Walls in Angola

LEGEND

The Lioness and the Ostrich
(San)

Long ago a lioness heard that ostriches could roar. Being a vain creature, she invited the ostrich to join her in a roaring contest. The ostrich let out a loud, thundering roar. Then the lioness took her turn. Both roars were equal in strength and sound. The dejected lioness realized that the ostrich was her match.

The lioness knew her hunting skills were greater than those of the ostrich. "Let's go on a hunt together and see who is the best hunter," she said. To the lioness's dismay, the ostrich killed many animals, but she killed just one.

The lioness's young cubs grew hungry watching their mother and the ostrich compete. "It's time to eat our kill," the lioness said. "Go and rip the meat for both you and your children," the ostrich replied. "When you are full I will drink the blood." After the meal the lioness, her cubs, and the ostrich took a nap.

The cubs woke early and began to play near the ostrich. They looked at the ostrich, who slept with his mouth open. To the cubs' amazement they found he had no teeth.

"Mother," the cubs whispered. "Wake up. The ostrich has no teeth and is pretending to be your equal. He is making a fool of you." The angry lioness woke up the ostrich. "Get up now," she said. "Let's fight to see who is strongest."

"All right," the sly ostrich said. "Go to one side of that anthill and I will go to the other." As the lioness stood ready to pounce, the ostrich knocked over the anthill. Ants quickly swarmed over the lioness. Then the ostrich kicked her in a vulnerable spot and she died.

Who is smarter, the ostrich or the lioness? Do you think being clever requires sharp teeth and a powerful body?

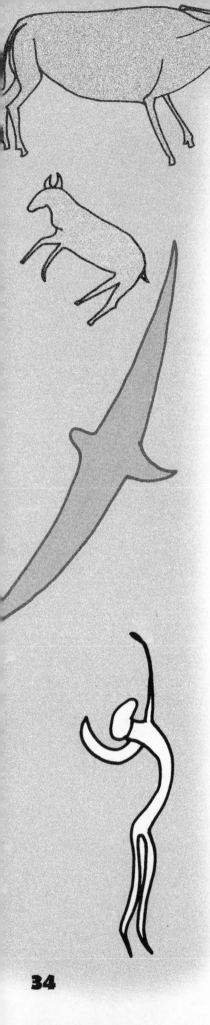

Group Project

Pictograph Sandstone Tiles (San)

The San were prolific cave painters. Many paintings seem to depict scenes of hunting or of daily life. The San made brushes from the tails or manes of wildebeests, which they attached to pointed bones or antelope horns. Paints were made by mixing earth pigments with binding materials such as animal fat, milk, honey, or urine. The San stored paint in ostrich eggs. To protect the finished paintings, the San covered them with tree-bark resin.

Before You Begin

- Distribute and discuss the Pictograph Designs page. If possible, share other books on San pictographs.
- Compare ancient peoples' pictographs. For instance, Native Americans of California and the Far North drew designs for religious purposes. The San, however, seemed more concerned with portraying daily life and struggles.
- Encourage students to brainstorm images associated with their daily lives and compare them with those created by the San.
- Have students paint with "found" items such as sharpened sticks, feathers, or even cleaned and dried chicken bones. They might also use paint containers made of cleaned and dried eggshells.

Materials (for each student)

- 3 cups (720 ml) plaster of Paris
- 1/2 cup (120 ml) sand or small gravel
- water
- mixing container
- plastic rectangular container, 6 x 9 inches (15 x 22.5 cm)
- acrylic or poster paints: white, black, rust, yellow
- paintbrushes or natural materials for applying paint
- newspapers
- carbon paper
- tape

34

To Make Sandstone Tiles

1. Lay newspapers down to protect surface. Mix plaster of Paris, sand, and water to make the consistency of pudding.
2. Pour mixture into plastic container. Let dry. When plaster is curing, it feels warm to the touch.
3. Make sure plaster is completely set and no longer warm. Slowly twist both sides of the plastic container until the tile pops out. Dry thoroughly. (Figure 1)

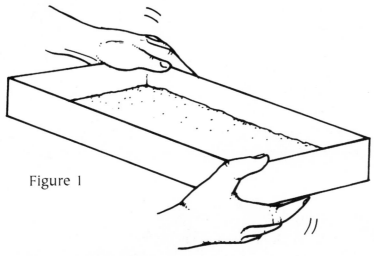

Figure 1

To Design the Pictograph

4. Choose a pictograph design or draw another design.
5. Draw the design on the tile. Or place a sheet of carbon paper between the design and tile. Tape down. (Figure 2)
6. If using carbon paper, trace lines of design on tile. The drawing does not have to be accurate but should tell a clear story.
7. Paint in the design on the tile. Use found objects to make the process more authentic.

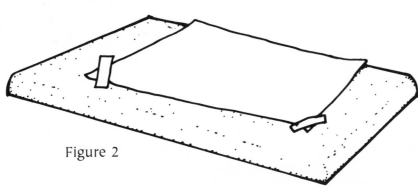

Figure 2

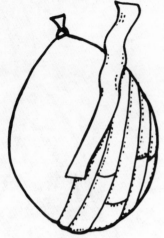

Figure 1

Individual Project

Ostrich-Egg Painting (San)

The San sometimes decorated their precious ostrich eggs with pictograph designs.

Materials (for each student)

- oval balloon
- newspapers
- wallpaper paste
- 1 cup (240 ml) plaster of Paris
- fine sandpaper
- acrylic or poster paints
- brushes

1. Mix wallpaper paste according to directions. Rip newspaper into small strips.
2. Inflate and tie balloon. It should be a good-sized oval.
3. Moisten newspaper strips with paste and lay across balloon. Cover balloon and let dry. (Figure 1)
4. Cut a 1-inch (2.5-cm) hole on the top of the dried paper balloon. (Figure 2)
5. Lightly sand rough surface areas.
6. Mix plaster of Paris in a separate container. Smear a scoop onto the paper egg. Smooth wet plaster down with your hands. Continue until whole egg is covered. (Figure 3)
7. Stand the egg upside down, with the hole against the table. Let dry. (Figure 4).
8. Turn the egg over, with the hole upright. Paint pictograph designs on it. (Figure 5)

Figure 2

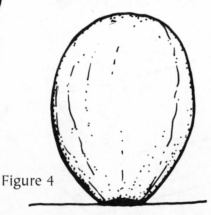

Figure 3

Figure 4

Figure 5

36

People of Southwest Africa

Pictograph Designs (San)

People of Southwest Africa

Garments to Color (San)

Color the traditional garments by following the key below.

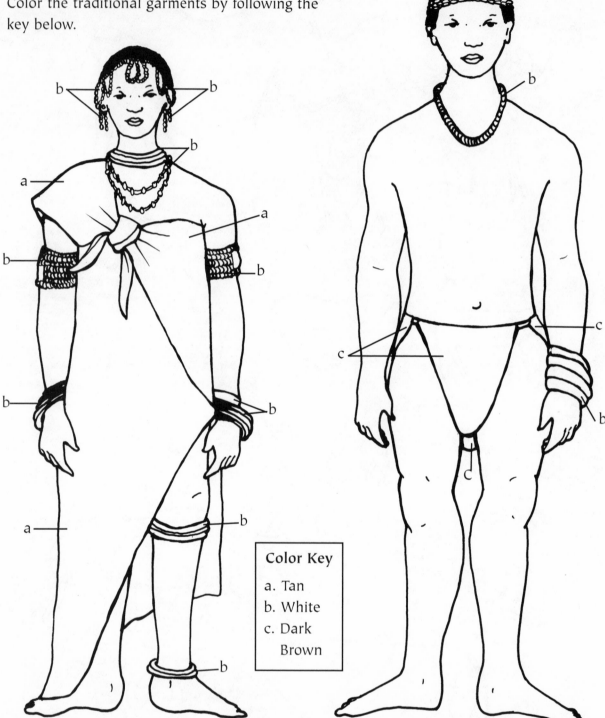

Color Key

a. Tan
b. White
c. Dark Brown

(Teacher's note: Use this page as a flat coloring sheet or enlarge each item to use in one of the special projects described on pages 6-7.)

People of Southwest Africa

Tools and Dwellings to Color (San)

Color each item by using the key below.

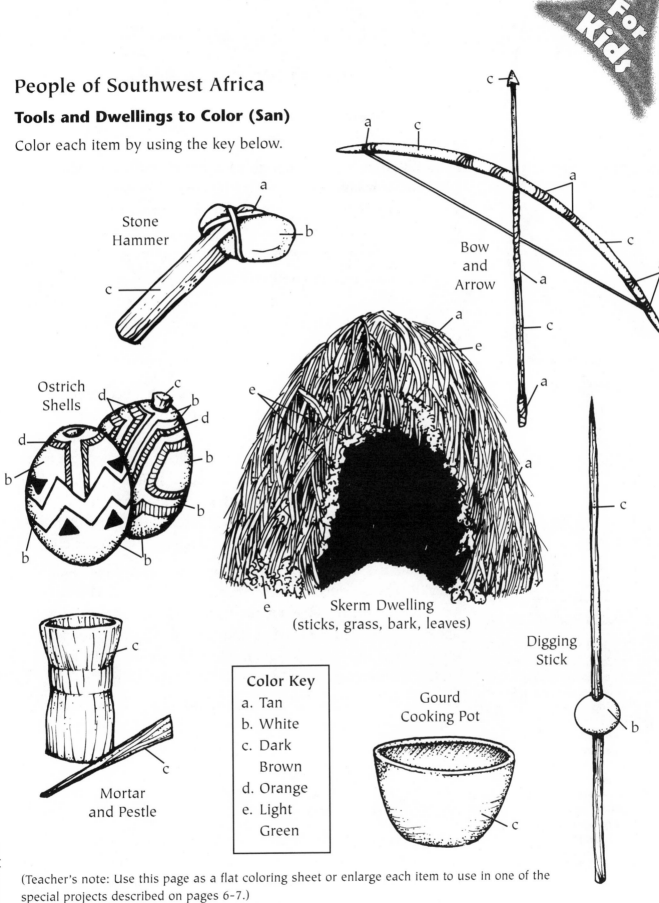

Stone Hammer

Bow and Arrow

Ostrich Shells

Skerm Dwelling
(sticks, grass, bark, leaves)

Digging Stick

Mortar and Pestle

Color Key
a. Tan
b. White
c. Dark Brown
d. Orange
e. Light Green

Gourd Cooking Pot

(Teacher's note: Use this page as a flat coloring sheet or enlarge each item to use in one of the special projects described on pages 6-7.)

39

X

Copper Ingot Found in the Zambezi Valley. The copper was this shape so that bearers could carry it more easily on shoulder sticks.

People of Southern Africa

Background Information

Botswana, Zambia, Zimbabwe, and Malawi are landlocked countries of southern and southeastern Africa. Swaziland and Mozambique border the Indian Ocean. South Africa borders the Atlantic and the Indian Oceans. The southern Africa coastline is covered with wooded shrubland, which changes to dry savannas and deserts further inland.

Thousands of Bantu-speaking people lived in southern Africa. The dominant groups were the **Zulu**, **Swazi**, **Shona**, **Ndebele**, **Tswana**, **Sotho**, and **Basuto**.

Daily Life

Archaeologists believe the San inhabited southern Africa nearly 20,000 years ago. The Khoikhoi arrived shortly after. They shared a language called Khoisan. From about A.D. 700 to 1000, huge migrations of Bantu-speaking people from the northwest and Congo regions settled in southern Africa. They outnumbered the Khoisan and were skilled at forging metals into weapons. The San and Khoikhoi were forced to fight the Bantu, move into less-inhabited deserts, or merge into Bantu society.

Many Bantu-speaking groups lived in homesteads called kraals, individual huts protected by brush and wood fences. The walls and floors of the huts were made from a mixture of anthills, soil, and cow dung. The roofs were made of dry grass and weeds. In the center of the kraal was a fenced enclosure for cattle, to protect the livestock from thieves and wild predators.

These Bantu-speaking groups ate two meals a day, based on the hours in which cattle were taken to and returned from the fields. The Bantu diet included sorghum, millet, yams, sugarcane, watermelon, gourds, and *amasi*, or curdled milk. Pumpkin and peanuts were added after the fifteenth century. The Bantu ate cattle only on special occasions.

Zulu men of particular distinction wore head rings made of tree fungus. Eventually the head rings would harden. They were never removed. The women decorated their necks, arms, and ankles with brass and copper rings called *iindzilas*. These ornaments, too, were never removed.

FACT

Shona Manners
• Clapping hands was a gesture of thanks when receiving a gift. Taking the gift with both hands symbolized that the gift was large and generous, no matter how small it really was.
• To show respect, young people would sit or squat when speaking to elders.

Customs and Beliefs

Swazi infants were secluded from outsiders for as long as one month. Only the mother, wet nurse, or medicine man could see the baby. Fathers were not allowed to visit the baby for fear that evil spirits might be attached to him. The higher the father's warrior status, the more spirits he carried. At the age of three months, the child was given a name and introduced to the world.

Cattle were the Bantu's most important possession. Cattle were considered intermediaries between this world and the spirit world. Before an animal was sacrificed, it was given a message to carry to the owner's ancestors. Cattle were considered beautiful and were the subjects of poems. Owners often had a favorite steer and treated it as a pet.

The desire for cattle also caused many wars, which were often started by surprise attacks. Groups stole cattle from each other and also stole children, women, and booty. Unmarried girls were taken to become wives. The ongoing battles increased people's fears and anxieties.

The Rise and Fall of Kingdoms

The Great Zimbabwe Kingdom began around the thirteenth century A.D. and lasted for nearly 350 years. A rich kingdom, it was built upon the trading of gold, ivory, and copper. The capital contained huge conical towers, great curving walls, and pillars built of perfectly cut stone. Builders constructed these famous structures without using nails or mortar. However, Great Zimbabwe is shrouded with mystery. Archaeologists are not sure who built the kingdom, where they came from, or why they disappeared. Some believe that a great drought caused the first inhabitants to abandon the sites.

During the eighteenth century, another drought caused a famine that prompted raids and

Xhosa Pipe

FACT

Zulu women wore body creams and lipstick made from vegetable oils mixed with hippopotamus fat and herbs.

FACT

Visitors had to stop at the entrance of a village and announce their arrival. They could not enter without approval.

Ndebele Courtyard Wall

Sotho Horn
Container

rivalry among the Bantu. By 1819 a Zulu warrior named Shaka had become a powerful leader. Shaka's military strategies, discipline, and fighting techniques enabled his army to dominate southern Africa. Shaka also refined the long-throwing spears, called *assegais*, into shorter weapons for close-contact fighting.

Shaka wanted peace for his people, but his quest to build a kingdom and control the entire territory left millions homeless and starving. This period in African history is called *Mfecane*, which means "The Crushing." Eventually even Shaka's most avid followers saw that he had gone too far. At the age of 41, Shaka was murdered by his half-brother.

Arrival of Europeans

The Arabs, Portuguese, British, and Dutch came to southern Africa to trade. By the 1700s, thousands of Dutch Boers took over the land for farming. The Dutch pushed the displaced Khoisan into the Namib and Kalahari Deserts. Meanwhile the British navy established a base off the coast of what is now South Africa. Their domination forced the Bantu, Khoisan, and Dutch further inland.

In 1869, diamonds were found in what is now South Africa. Thousands of speculators from Australia, Europe, and the Americas converged on this region. Great Britain quickly annexed the country for itself and wrested control of much of the Bantu land. The infiltration of foreigners disturbed the traditional Bantu lifestyle and wars ensued. Because of an ongoing famine and internal civil wars, the Africans could not defeat the British.

FACT

Sotho girls carried beaded dolls during their wedding ceremony. The doll was named and carried by the bride until the first child was born. The doll's name was then transferred to the child.

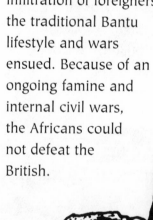

Ruins of the Great Zambezi

LEGEND

The Lost Immortal and His Feast of Peace
(Zulu)

One day the Lost Immortal met with the Bantu people. "I will deliver you from war but you must trust and obey me," he said, and the people agreed. He captured all the warring chiefs and had his wives and daughters make a stew out of them. From that moment all the fighting stopped.

The Lost Immortal instructed his people to prepare a grand feast. Men cut down trees and made huts, kraals, bowls, spoons, forks, drums, marimbas, and many other wooden objects. Others hunted food and collected roots and berries. Former enemies now worked side by side as friends. People from distant lands walked for days to participate in the festivities. Everyone dressed in elaborate clothes. The Lost Immortal was very pleased.

When the festivities began, warriors from every nation lined up to perform a breathtaking parade of unity. People rose to their feet at the sound of the drums. Ten warriors from each regiment helped carry a huge stone of peace to be placed in front of the Lost Immortal. The stone was inscribed "These great nations have taken an oath of peace. All respect this peace." Everyone was filled with hope.

In turn, each warrior laid down his shield and assegai, or spear, and replaced it with a tree branch. People sang, danced, and feasted as the assegais were broken. Each warrior cut his thumb and forefinger and let the blood drip into bowls, merging with others'. The men passed the bowls to other warriors, saying, "You are my brother; I am yours."

At the end of the festivities, the warriors gathered around the great stone and dropped it inside a hole. They covered it with the dirt of a thousand hoes. And peace was built for a thousand years.

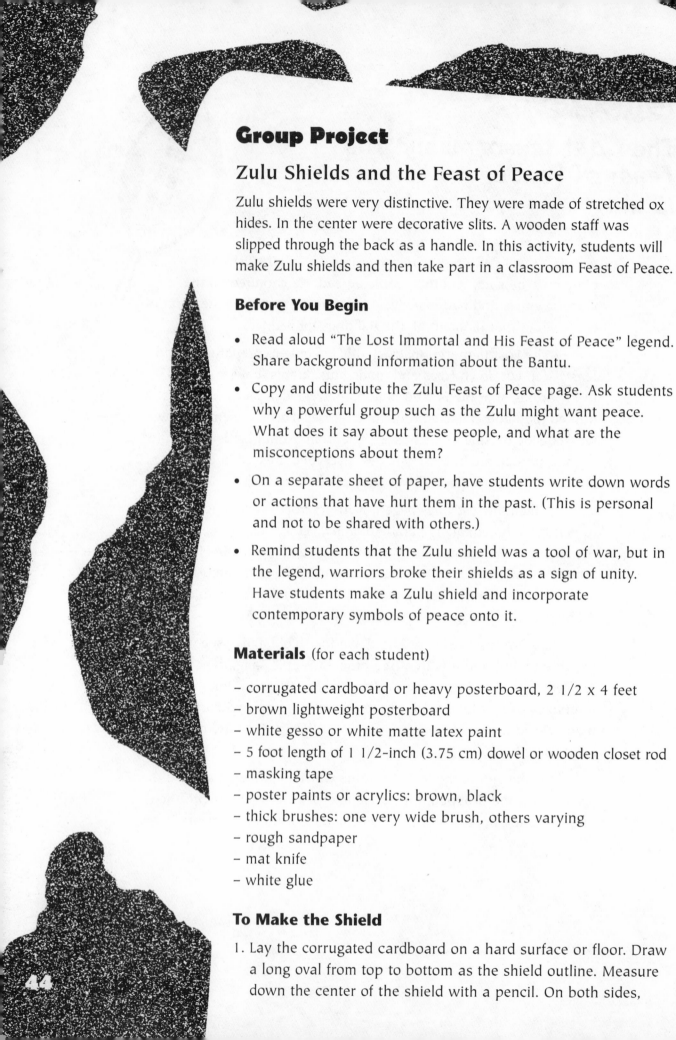

Group Project

Zulu Shields and the Feast of Peace

Zulu shields were very distinctive. They were made of stretched ox hides. In the center were decorative slits. A wooden staff was slipped through the back as a handle. In this activity, students will make Zulu shields and then take part in a classroom Feast of Peace.

Before You Begin

- Read aloud "The Lost Immortal and His Feast of Peace" legend. Share background information about the Bantu.

- Copy and distribute the Zulu Feast of Peace page. Ask students why a powerful group such as the Zulu might want peace. What does it say about these people, and what are the misconceptions about them?

- On a separate sheet of paper, have students write down words or actions that have hurt them in the past. (This is personal and not to be shared with others.)

- Remind students that the Zulu shield was a tool of war, but in the legend, warriors broke their shields as a sign of unity. Have students make a Zulu shield and incorporate contemporary symbols of peace onto it.

Materials (for each student)

- corrugated cardboard or heavy posterboard, 2 1/2 x 4 feet
- brown lightweight posterboard
- white gesso or white matte latex paint
- 5 foot length of 1 1/2-inch (3.75 cm) dowel or wooden closet rod
- masking tape
- poster paints or acrylics: brown, black
- thick brushes: one very wide brush, others varying
- rough sandpaper
- mat knife
- white glue

To Make the Shield

1. Lay the corrugated cardboard on a hard surface or floor. Draw a long oval from top to bottom as the shield outline. Measure down the center of the shield with a pencil. On both sides,

Figure 1

draw several horizontal 4-x-1-inch (10-x-2.5-cm) rectangles, evenly spaced. (Figure 1)

2. Cut out the shield with a mat knife. Do the same with the rectangles.

3. Tape around the edges with masking tape. Cover the entire shield and masked edges with a thick coat of gesso. Let dry. (Figure 2)

Figure 2

4. Sand the edges until smooth. Apply another coat of gesso. Let dry.

5. Cut the brown posterboard into long strips, 5 inches (12.5 cm) wide. Glue them to the back of the shield, making sure they show through the rectangle slits. (Figure 3)

Figure 3

6. Align the bottom of the dowel with the bottom of the shield. Center the dowel horizontally. Tape and glue dowel in place. The top part of the dowel should rise 1 foot above shield. (Figure 4)

7. Paint black and brown splotches to resemble the spots of a cow. (Figure 5)

Figure 4

8. Have students roll their written problems and resolutions and secure them to the pole with a piece of twine. Display the shields in the classroom.

The Feast of Peace

Meet as a class and sit on floor mats. Invite students to bring potluck meals. Have each student pass around a bowl of milk, symbolizing the sacred cattle. In the legend, people shared meals during the feast as acts of peace, friendship, and kinship.

Have students share their views of how people can resolve conflicts peacefully. Invite students to take their "past hurts" papers, fold them, and secure them with a rubber band to a rock. Students may wish to bury the rocks in a pail filled with soil.

Figure 5

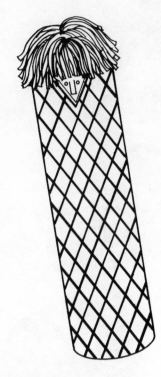

Individual Project

Zulu Doll

The Zulu made beautiful beaded objects. Originally, beads were made from ostrich shells and wood. Glass beads were introduced through trade with East African merchants, who brought them from India.

Materials

- 12-inch (30 cm) length of shipping tube, 3 inches (7.5 cm) in diameter
- white glue
- acrylic or poster paints: white, green, pink, light blue, yellow, black
- black marker
- natural-colored raffia, available in craft stores

To Make the Doll

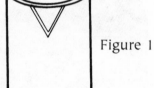

Figure 1

1. Draw a 1-inch (2.5-cm) V on the tube for the doll's face. (Figure 1)

2. Draw diagonal lines around the tube, 1 inch (2.5 cm) apart. (Figure 2)

3. Draw diagonal lines in the opposite direction, touching the lines drawn in Step 2. You should have diamond shapes around the tube. (Figure 3)

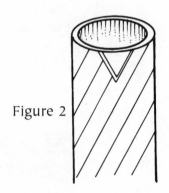

Figure 2

4. Use different colors to paint within diamond outlines. Let dry.

5. Outline diamonds with a black marker. Draw the eyes. (Figure 4)

6. Cut raffia in 3-inch (7.5-cm) clumps. Glue ends inside the end of the tube and fold over to hang. Continue until hole is filled and raffia hair sticks out. Trim to desired length. (Figure 5)

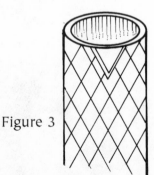

Figure 3

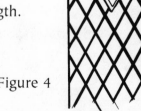

Figure 4

Figure 5

46

People of Southern Africa

Zulu Feast of Peace

The Feast of Peace described in the Zulu legend represents the desire for former enemies to set aside their grievances, share new ideas, and appreciate one another. Here is what the symbols represent.

Kraal: This is a community meeting place where people shared thoughts, ideas, and grievances peacefully.

Assegai (Spear): Broken spears also represented the desire for peace.

Shield: Warriors laid down their shields to show they wanted peace.

Rock: It represented the heavy burden of hatred that people carried inside them. By burying it they buried their differences and gained peace.

Tree Branch: Warriors replaced their shields and spears with tree branches, perhaps to symbolize life.

Bowl: In the legend, bowls held drops of warriors' blood. This symbolized an act of kinship and brotherly love. During the classroom feast, milk will be used instead.

Food: The Bantu met as a large extended family having a holiday meal, sharing food, small talk, and celebration.

People of Southern Africa

Garments to Color (Zulu)

Color the traditional garments by following the key below.

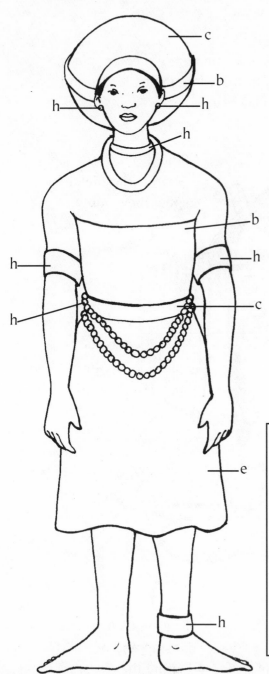

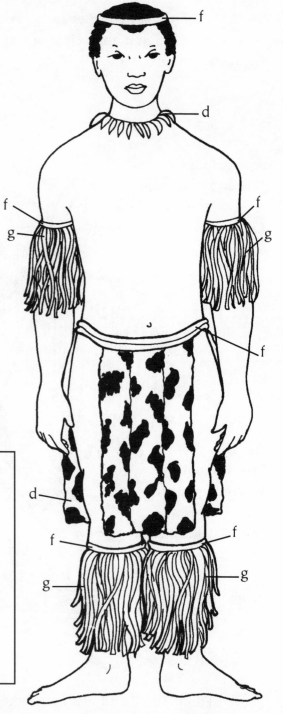

Color Key

a. Red
b. Green
c. Yellow
d. White
e. Blue
f. Brown
g. Tan
h. Gold or Copper

(Teacher's note: Use this page as a flat coloring sheet or enlarge each item to use in one of the special projects described on pages 6-7.)

People of Southern Africa

Tools and Dwellings to Color

Color each item by using the color key below.

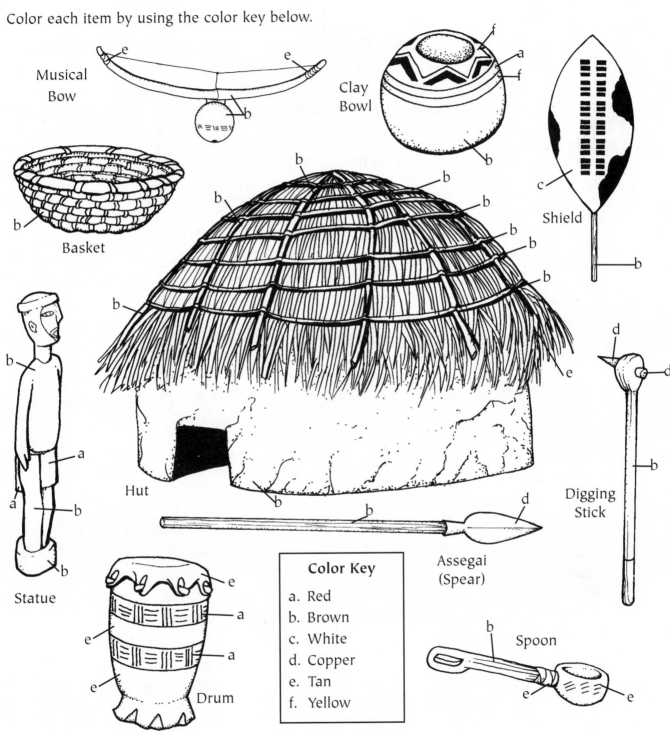

Musical Bow

Clay Bowl

Shield

Basket

Hut

Statue

Drum

Assegai (Spear)

Digging Stick

Spoon

Color Key

a. Red
b. Brown
c. White
d. Copper
e. Tan
f. Yellow

(Teacher's note: Use this page as a flat coloring sheet or enlarge each item to use in one of the special projects described on pages 6-7.)

49

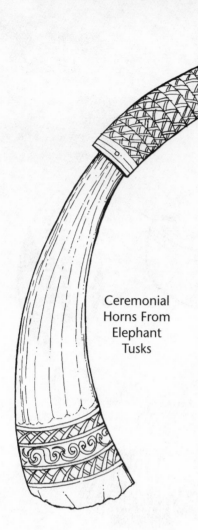

Ceremonial
Horns From
Elephant
Tusks

People of East Africa

Background Information

In East Africa the Horn of Africa juts into the Red Sea, the Gulf of Aden, and the Indian Ocean. Ethiopia, Djibouti, Eritrea, Somalia, Kenya, and Tanzania border these waters. Further inland are Uganda, Rwanda, and Burundi. The landscape varies from dry wooded savannas to grasslands to the high plateaus of the Great Rift Valley.

At one time the major groups of East Africa were the **Nilotics**, **Bantu**, **Cushites**, and **Pygmoids**.

Migrations and Early Inhabitants

A Pygmoid group called the Twa were the first known inhabitants of east central Africa. The Twa were forest-dwelling hunters and gatherers.

About 15,000 years ago, Khoisan-speaking groups inhabited East Africa. It was not until 1000 B.C. that the first migrations of Cushite-speaking people began. The Cushites came from Ethiopia and merged with the local people. Over time they developed into such groups as the Oromo and Somali.

Much later, in the fifteenth century A.D., Bantu groups moved to this region from central Africa. The Bantu-speaking Hutu, Swahili, and Kenye developed fishing and farming communities.

Nilotics migrated from the north between the fifteenth and eighteenth centuries A.D. They included the Suk, Tutsi, and Masai. They had a pastoral lifestyle.

Daily Life and Trading Patterns

The Swahili were skilled sailors. They navigated boats of wooden planks lashed together with palm fiber rope. They journeyed up and down the Red Sea and traded with the Egyptians, Romans, and Phoenicians.

Beginning in the first century A.D., Arab traders traveled to East Africa in search of ivory and gold. Over time, Arabs merged with

Masai girls had their earlobes cut and stretched with wads of grass as a sign of beauty. They also made decorative cuts in their faces.

the Swahili and other East African groups. The East Africans adopted Islam and integrated Arab customs, laws, and poetry into their existing societies. Swahili, made up of African and Arabic words and grammar, later became the lingua franca of this trading region.

Wealthy Swahili built huge Arab-influenced dwellings and mosques. They constructed sunken courtyards with sculptured gardens and installed indoor plumbing. The buildings were made of coral bricks. The aristocracy wore Chinese silk and cotton. They also minted silver, copper, and gold coins.

Cows were the Masai's most important possession. They ate cow meat only on special occasions. At certain times of the year, a main staple of their diet was cow milk mixed with blood drawn from a cow's jugular vein. This mixture provided vitamins and proteins not found in other parts of their diet.

The Masai lived in kraals. As cattle herders, they had a seminomadic lifestyle, traveling in search of fresh water and grazing land. They often fought to dominate the land and to steal cattle from others. The Masai gained the reputation of being fierce warriors.

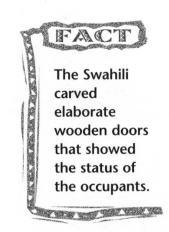

FACT

The Swahili carved elaborate wooden doors that showed the status of the occupants.

Customs and Beliefs

Pastoral groups of East Africa invested important symbolism in milk, blood, and grass. During council meetings, men would drink a mixture of cow milk and blood to reinforce group unity. Grass was used as a sign of peace. A man who wore a tuft of it on his head was spared death during battles or raids.

The Swahili—a mixed group from many backgrounds—converted to Islam at least as early as the seventh century A.D. They built mosques and studied the Koran. Christianity had less of an impact on the region. However, in the sixth century, Christianity spread to Ethiopia, where great Coptic cathedrals were built.

Swahili Decorated Doors

Ethiopian
Illustrated
Manuscript of
the Gospel

The Kingdom of Axum

Around 220 B.C., the powerful kingdom of Axum emerged in Ethiopia. It was known for its beautiful architecture, government, intellectual society, wealthy citizens, and strong military power. The grandeur of Axum rivaled the Nubian and Kemet Kingdoms of the north.

The kingdom had easy access to land and sea routes. Trade with ancient Egyptians lasted from 333 B.C. (possibly even earlier) to A.D. 50. Axumites also traded with the early Romans. Able sailors, the Axumites kept the Red Sea safe from Arab pirates.

By A.D. 100, Axum was the strongest empire in the area. It controlled trade from Africa to Asia, China, India, and Sri Lanka. Axum engulfed the Kemet and Nubian Kingdoms. It became so powerful that it was able to invade and rule the Arabian peninsula for almost 50 years. During the sixth century, Axum was a Christian kingdom. It flourished until it was absorbed into Africa's Islamic world, but Christianity and Judaism persisted in this area into modern times.

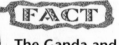

FACT

The Ganda and Tutsi were noted for their beautiful straw mats and room screens, decorated with geometric designs.

Arrival of Europeans

During the 1400s the Portuguese were searching for new trade routes that would take them to India and Arabia without encountering Muslim rivals. In 1498 the Portuguese reached East Africa from the south. They encountered wealthy Swahili cities whose exotic wares included Indian spices, silks, perfumes, and other luxuries.

The Portuguese were determined to seize control of this region. They demanded that the Swahili pay allegiance to the king of Portugal with huge amounts of goods and wealth. Those who refused were attacked. After many battles the Portuguese dominated the area. They controlled East African trade for the next century.

Swahili
Writing

How the Masai Got Their Cattle

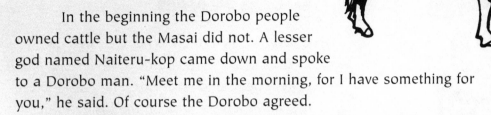

In the beginning the Dorobo people owned cattle but the Masai did not. A lesser god named Naiteru-kop came down and spoke to a Dorobo man. "Meet me in the morning, for I have something for you," he said. Of course the Dorobo agreed.

A Masai man named Le-eyo was hiding nearby and overheard their conversation. He could hardly wait for nightfall so he could sneak to the place mentioned by Naiteru-kop. In the long, dark hours, Le-eyo waited while the Dorobo man slept comfortably in his hut.

At dawn the lesser god saw the Masai but was confused. "Who are you and where is the Dorobo?" he asked. "My name is Le-eyo," the Masai man said. "I don't know where the Dorobo is, but I am here for you instead."

Naiteru-kop shrugged. He took a leather thong and lowered his cattle from the sky, one by one. Soon there were so many cattle that Le-eyo pleaded for Naiteru-kop to stop.

Some of the cattle wandered off. And the Dorobo man, who had finally awakened, raced to catch them. He knew that these cattle were rightfully his. He grew furious when he realized that Naiteru-kop had given his people's cattle to the Masai.

The Dorobo and his people grabbed their bows and arrows and shot at the leather thong that still hung in the sky. This action infuriated Naiteru-kop so much that he moved to a distant land and never again gave the Dorobo cattle. After this the Masai owned all the cattle, and the Dorobo were left to hunt wild animals with bows and arrows.

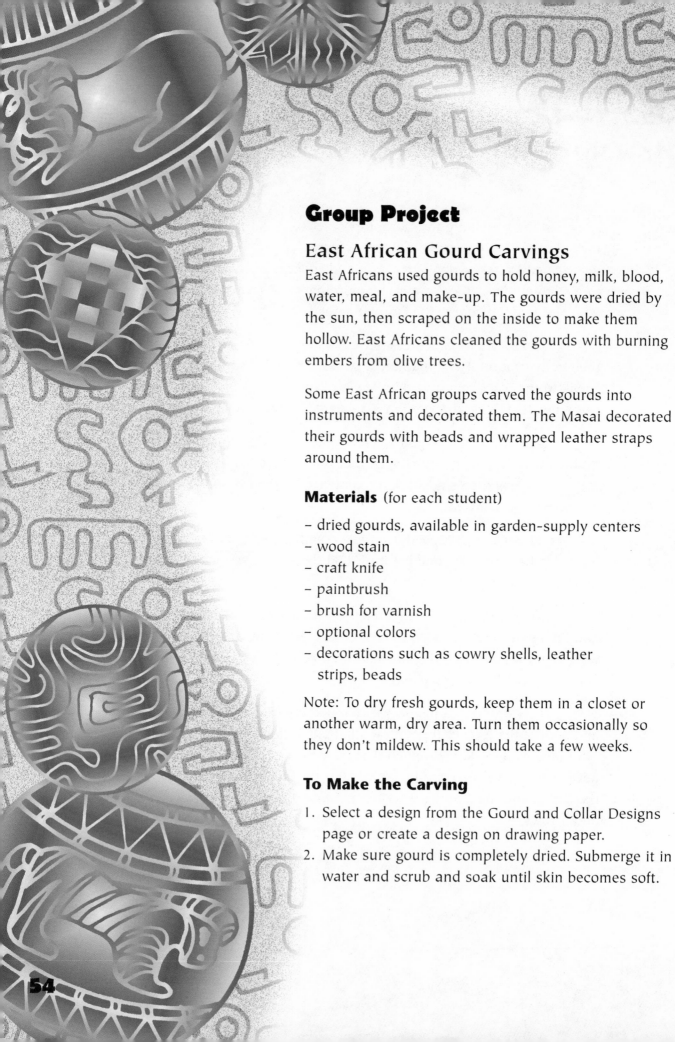

Group Project

East African Gourd Carvings

East Africans used gourds to hold honey, milk, blood, water, meal, and make-up. The gourds were dried by the sun, then scraped on the inside to make them hollow. East Africans cleaned the gourds with burning embers from olive trees.

Some East African groups carved the gourds into instruments and decorated them. The Masai decorated their gourds with beads and wrapped leather straps around them.

Materials (for each student)

- dried gourds, available in garden-supply centers
- wood stain
- craft knife
- paintbrush
- brush for varnish
- optional colors
- decorations such as cowry shells, leather strips, beads

Note: To dry fresh gourds, keep them in a closet or another warm, dry area. Turn them occasionally so they don't mildew. This should take a few weeks.

To Make the Carving

1. Select a design from the Gourd and Collar Designs page or create a design on drawing paper.
2. Make sure gourd is completely dried. Submerge it in water and scrub and soak until skin becomes soft.

Scrub with rough
steel wool to remove outer
skin. Draw design on gourd.
(Figure 1)

3. Choose parts of design to
   darken with stain. Apply stain.
   Let dry.

Figure 1

4. Cut out the outlines. The cuts will show lighter
   flesh of gourd. This process will help the natural
   color of the gourd show through against the stain.
   Make sure you do not cut too deeply into gourd.
   (Figure 2)

5. Apply one to two
   coats of varnish. Let
   dry between coats.

Figure 2

6. Glue or attach
   decorations such as cowry
   shells, leather strips,
   or beads.

Individual Project

Masai Collar Necklaces

Both Masai women and men wore jewelry. Women wore heavy collared pieces made with beads and copper wire. Men wore several lightweight necklaces that dangled freely.

Before You Begin

Ask students what types of jewelry men and women wear today and compare them with those worn by the Masai.

Materials (for each student)

- two corrugated cardboard circles, 18-inch (45-cm) and 16-inch (40-cm) diameters
- masking tape
- white latex paint or acrylic gesso
- large paintbrush
- scissors
- sandpaper
- acrylic or poster paint: red, blue, green, orange, black, yellow
- small glass beads (optional)
- small pasta or orzo dyed with food coloring (optional)

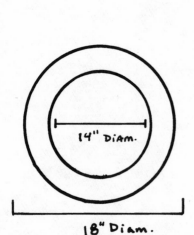

14" Diam.

18" Diam.

Figure 1

1. Cut a 14-inch- (35-cm-) diameter circle inside the 18-inch (45-cm) cardboard circle. (Figure 1)
2. Cut a 7-inch- (17.5-cm-) diameter circle inside the 16-inch (40-cm) cardboard circle.
3. Cut a slit on one side of each collar so head can slip through. (Figure 2)
4. Tape edges and cover with two coats of gesso. Let dry. Sand to make edges smooth.
5. Choose designs from the Gourd and Collar Designs page or draw designs on paper.
6. Paint designs on each collar with various colors. Let dry and wear. Or make a textured design by gluing on collars small pasta or orzo dyed with food coloring.

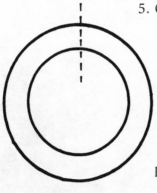

CUT

Figure 2

People of East Africa

Gourd and Collar Designs

Many East African geometric designs and circular patterns
represented animals and reptiles.

People of East Africa

Garments to Color (Masai)

Color the traditional garments by following the key below.

e a c
c

b

e b c a
c a
b e
a
c a

e

a

b
c

c

d d
b b b
d
d d

c e c
c
c

a a

f
f

d
d
d

a

a

c

c
c

d d
f
f

f f

Color Key

a. Red
b. White
c. Blue
d. Copper
e. Green
f. Tan

(Teacher's note: Use this page as a flat coloring sheet or enlarge each item to use in one of the special projects described on pages 6-7.)

People of East Africa

Tools and Dwellings to Color (Masai)

Color the tools and dwellings by following the key below.

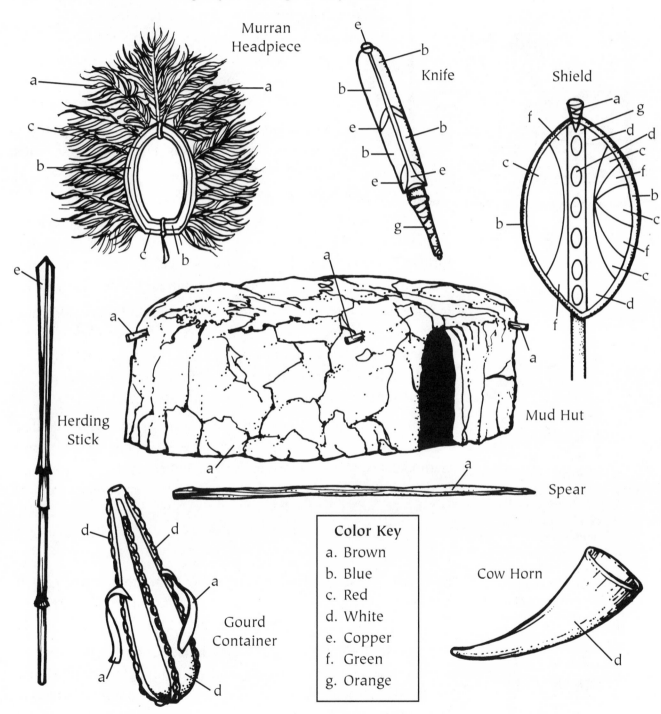

Murran Headpiece

Knife

Shield

Herding Stick

Mud Hut

Spear

Gourd Container

Cow Horn

Color Key
a. Brown
b. Blue
c. Red
d. White
e. Copper
f. Green
g. Orange

(Teacher's note: Use this page as a flat coloring sheet or enlarge each item to use in one of the special projects described on pages 6-7.)

Coptic Art

People of Northeast Africa

Background Information

Northeast Africa encompasses the countries now known as Egypt and Sudan. The Nile River cuts through this region, eventually spilling into the Mediterranean Sea. The Red Sea lies on the coast of Egypt and northeast Sudan. The landscape includes deserts, tropical rain forests, grasslands, and swamps.

At one time, some of the major groups in this region were the **Nubians**, **Nuer**, **Dinkas**, **Egyptians**, and **Arabs**.

Early Migrations and Kingdoms

It is believed that around 5000 B.C., ancient hunters and gatherers moved into this region to escape land that was slowly turning to desert. They lived in scattered villages along the banks of the Nile. They controlled the river's annual floods with canals.

In 3000 B.C., kingdoms grew along the Upper and Lower Nile due to extensive trading up and down the river. They developed new farming techniques, shipbuilding, writing, and medicines. By 2686 B.C., the kingdoms came under the rule of the pharaohs, and the great pyramids were built.

Ancient Egypt endured for more than 5,000 years and dominated Nubia (now southern Sudan) for much of that time. Despite constant clashes, the Nubians served as middlemen in a flourishing trade that linked Egypt with precious goods from Africa's tropical interior region.

Daily Life

Each year, monsoons and melting snow from Ethiopian mountains sent torrents of water and mud into the Nile. The waters flooded the basin and left behind fertile soil.

The Dinkas lived in mud-and-wattle huts, but during the wet season they moved their homes and cattle to high ground. When the floods subsided, they returned to the lower plains to harvest their crops.

FACT

Islamic governors of Egypt built a nilometer in A.D. 861 to measure the height of the Nile's annual floods. Engineers connected a brick pit to the river with tunnels. In the center of the pit stood a marker that determined the height of the flood.

The Nubians lived in small communities of several family huts. The huts had thatched roofs that were sometimes crowned with gourds or ostrich eggshells. Entrances were raised to keep out rodents and domestic animals. The Nubians' main crop was millet, and they also grew beans, cassavas, and sweet potatoes.

Wattle-and-Daub Hut

Egyptians kept cattle, sheep, and goats. They grew wheat, corn, radishes, cucumbers, and other vegetables. Rural Egyptians lived in houses made of wattle and daub, with mud and thatched roofs. In towns, homes were built of clay bricks. Wealthy Egyptians lived in large homes with brightly painted plaster walls. Their furniture was made of leather, reeds, cedar, or ebony.

Customs and Beliefs

Strong beliefs of immortality prevailed in both Egypt and Nubia. Pharaohs held absolute power, and everything centered around their well-being and glorification. It was believed that when pharaohs died, they would become gods. Pharaohs spent much of their time on ceremonial duties, and on trying to keep Upper and Lower Egypt united.

Life in a Nubian village centered around ceremonial wrestling. When a boy turned 13 or 14, he was sent to a wrestling camp several miles from his village. There he learned the art of wrestling and had high hopes for earning glory.

During the middle of the first

FACT

Papyrus paper was made from reeds growing by the Nile. Ancient Egyptians stripped the reeds of their bark and pounded the plants until they lay flat like paper. The paper was dried and glued together with a flour paste. The word *paper* comes from the word *papyrus*.

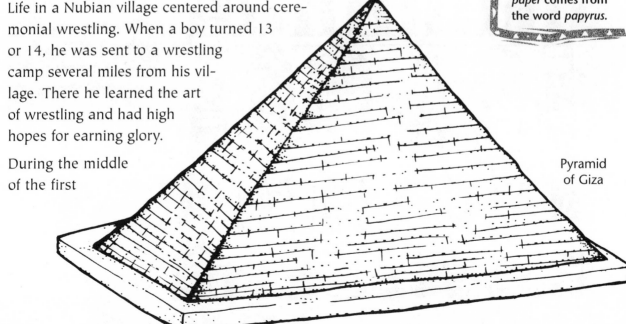

Pyramid of Giza

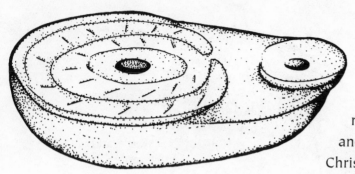

Oil Lamp, First Century A.D.

century, Christianity reached Egypt and slowly influenced Nubia. Christians in this region produced saints and built cathedrals and monasteries. In the seventh century, Christianity yielded to Arab Muslim conquests and crusades. Egyptians quickly adopted Islamic beliefs, customs, and traditions. However, it took longer for this faith to impact the Nubians.

Kingdoms and Invasions

In 30 B.C., the Roman Empire established Egypt as a province and ruled for the next seven centuries. Nubian kingdoms resisted the domination of the Roman Empire, and friction between the two was frequent. Fighting subsided in the first century A.D., when the Roman Emperor Justinian I established peace and sent Christian missionaries to what is now Sudan.

In 642, Arabs invaded Egypt, and Islam became the dominant religion. Although the invasion was a religious crusade, the Arabs also considered Egypt an important source of grain and other goods. Northeast Africa was ruled by Arab governors for seven centuries.

In 1517 the Egyptians and ruling Arabs were overwhelmed by an invasion from the Turkish Ottoman Empire. For the next three centuries, little changed under the Turkish rule, and Northeast Africa continued to maintain its adopted Arabic culture.

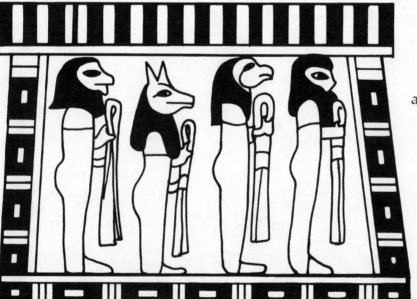

Cartonnage Fragment of the Four Sons of Horus

The Saint and the Serpent
(Coptic Egyptian)

A huge serpent lived near a village. Every year he threatened the people by saying he would stop the Nile from flowing if he did not receive a young girl as a sacrifice. The frightened villagers cast lots to find which girl would be sacrificed.

And so it was that the daughter of a king was chosen. The king was terribly sad when he found this out, but could do nothing to change it. On the appointed day the king followed his daughter and a procession of dancers and singers to the banks of the river. When they reached the river, the people left the girl to wait for the serpent.

God saw the girl and sent Saint Mari Girgis to help her. "Why are you alone?" the saint asked the girl. "Each year the serpent demands a girl to be sacrificed," she said. "I will wait here until he devours me. You must leave, otherwise your fate will be the same." The saint shook his head and said, "Do not be afraid, I will save you."

A while later the waters of the Nile began to gurgle and separate and the serpent emerged. The serpent laughed when he saw the saint and his tiny sword. As the serpent sprung up to devour the saint and the girl, Saint Mari Girgis swung his sword and killed the serpent.

Saint Mari Girgis and the girl carried the serpent back to the town. The terrified villagers were hiding in their homes. When they saw the girl and the saint, everyone ran outside and rejoiced. The king was so delighted that he wanted to give his daughter and his kingdom to Saint Mari Girgis. But Coptic saints never accept such gifts; they neither marry nor want worldly goods.

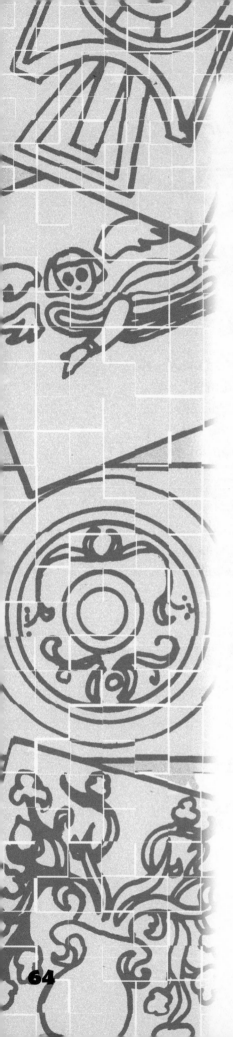

Group Project

Coptic Tiles

The middle of the first century A.D. marked the beginning of the Coptic period of northeast Africa. The Coptics developed a distinctive style based on Greco-Roman classical art.

Materials (for each student)

- porcelain bathroom tile
- acrylic paint: black, bluish purple, brown, magenta, yellow, green, red
- paintbrushes: 1 wide and flat; 1 fine-point
- Saral transfer paper
- sharp pencil
- vinegar
- paper towels

Optional Materials

- spray varnish
- 1/2-inch- (1.25-cm-) thick wood panel (length and width depend on the number of tiles)
- tile grout or white caulking

To Make Individual Tiles

1. Select a design from the Coptic Designs page or draw a design. Enlarge the design on a copier to fit on the tile.

2. Clean tile thoroughly with vinegar and water. Dry with a paper towel.

3. Lay transfer paper under design. Follow lines with a pencil. Avoid touching the surface of the tile, as it might prevent paint from adhering. (Figure 1)

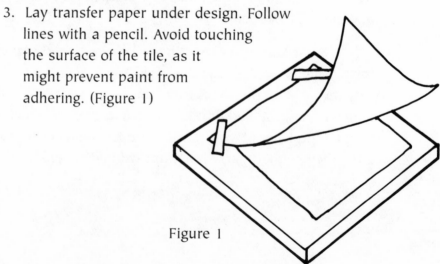

Figure 1

4. Use the fine-point brush to paint black outlines.

5. Dip the flat brush in water and load with a desired color for the inside shapes. Let dry between coats. Touch up black outlines where necessary.

6. To make the artwork permanent and dishwasher safe, place the tile on a cookie sheet and into a cold oven. Bake the tile at 325°F (165°C) for 35 to 40 minutes.

Note: You can use the paints without baking, but make sure to spray with a varnish to seal. This process makes the tiles semi-permanent. Be careful when cleaning with water.

To Make a Wall Display

7. Arrange tiles on a wooden board, approximately 1/2 inch (1.25 cm) thick. The size of the board depends upon the number of tiles. (Figure 2)

8. For a finished look, leave a 1/4-inch (.5 cm) space between each tile. Fill in with grout or white caulking. (Figure 3)

Figure 2

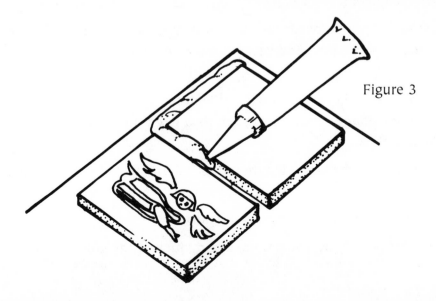

Figure 3

65

Individual Project

Coptic Masks

The Coptics of Roman Egypt continued the ancient tradition of ritual mummification, but the process became less extensive. The mummies' masks changed from elaborate Egyptian masks to Greco-Roman portraits. The newer masks were realistic stereotypes, not depictions of the deceased. The eyes were painted larger than normal. The faces were molded in plaster, then gilded and tilted forward. Laurel wreaths, jewelry, and other designs were either built with plaster or painted on.

Materials (for each student)

- plastic foam wig form
- large box of gauze or strips of newspaper
- gold spray paint
- acrylic paints: black, brown, green, white, blue, red
- shallow plastic basin
- plastic wrap
- plaster of Paris or papier-mâché mixture of flour, water, and white glue
- paintbrushes
- newspaper
- masking tape

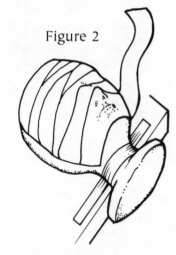

Figure 1

Figure 2

1. Choose a face design on the Coptic Designs page or create one. Use it as a model for the mask.

2. Wrap plastic wrap several times around the wig form and tape down. Lay the wig form on the edge of a table with its face facing upward. Secure it with tape to the table. (Figure 1)

3. Cover workspace with newspaper. Cut gauze into strips of varying size. Mix plaster of Paris in plastic basin, following directions on box. Keep consistency fairly thin.

4. Saturate gauze in plaster of Paris and lay across wig form. Cover front of head, sides, and neck with plaster strips. (Figure 2)

5. Build layers until head is 1/4 to 1/2 inch (.5 to 1.25 cm) thick. While plaster is wet, shape facial features such as the nose, eyes, and ears. Shape decorations such as a wreath or jewelry. Let dry. (Figure 3)

7. Once the plaster has dried thoroughly, stand the wig form upright and carefully cut away the plastic wrap from the back.

8. Spray mask with gold paint and let dry.

9. Paint mask with acrylic paints. Leave much of the gold exposed.

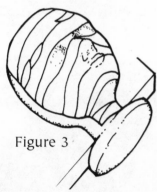

Figure 3

People of Northeast Africa

Coptic Designs

  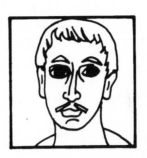 

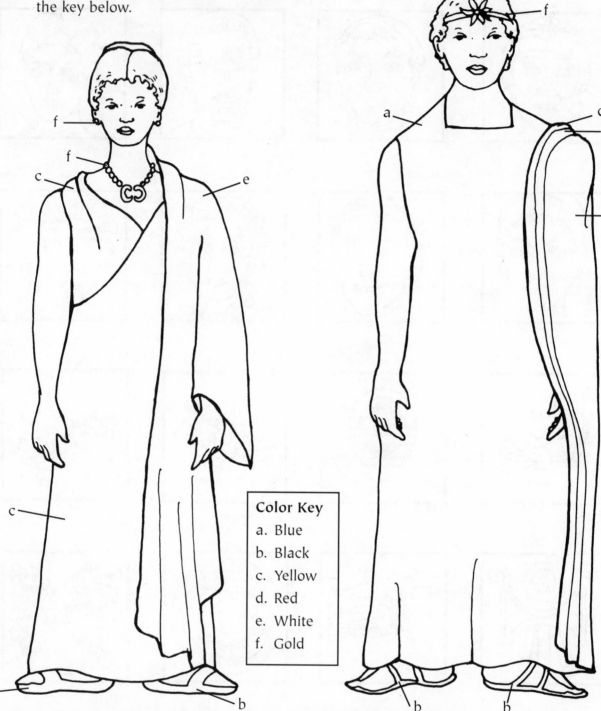

People of Northeast Africa

Garments to Color (Coptic Egyptian)

Color the traditional garments by following the key below.

Color Key
a. Blue
b. Black
c. Yellow
d. Red
e. White
f. Gold

(Teacher's note: Use this page as a flat coloring sheet or enlarge each item to use in one of the special projects described on pages 6-7.)

68

People of Northeast Africa

Tools and Dwellings to Color

Color each item by following the key below.

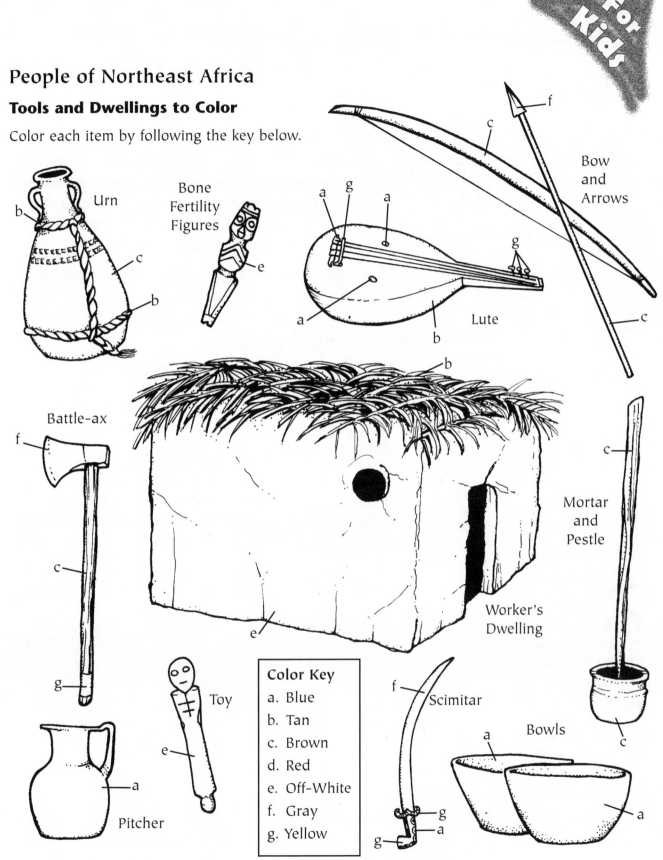

Urn

Bone Fertility Figures

Lute

Bow and Arrows

Battle-ax

Worker's Dwelling

Mortar and Pestle

Toy

Pitcher

Scimitar

Bowls

Color Key
a. Blue
b. Tan
c. Brown
d. Red
e. Off-White
f. Gray
g. Yellow

(Teacher's note: Use this page as a flat coloring sheet or enlarge each item to use in one of the special projects described on pages 6-7.)

Leather Cases
Carrying the
Koran

People of North Africa

Background Information

The North African countries of Western Sahara, Morocco, Algeria, Tunisia, and Libya border the Atlantic Ocean and the Mediterranean Sea. To the south lies the Sahara, a land of barren gravel plains, rocky mountains, and sand dunes that spans the continent.

At one time, some of the larger North African groups were the **Berbers**, **Bedouins**, and **Arabs**.

Migrations and Daily Life

The Sahara was once a lush, green land that supported ancient cattle herders and farmers. After 4000 B.C., the climate shifted, and endless droughts made the region less hospitable. People were forced to migrate to the outskirts of the savannas and other more inhabitable areas.

Toward the end of the second millennium B.C., aggressive Berber groups arrived, possibly from the Middle East. Berbers rode horses and carried javelins and shields, which aided them in their battles to control the land.

Coastal Berbers built dwellings with thatched roofs. They cultivated barley, wheat, and corn with sickles and wooden plows. Mountain Berbers built villages perched on hillsides.

Tuaregs were a large modern group of Berber nomads who lived in tents. The men wore blue garments and veils that covered their faces from the sand and sun. After camels were introduced to the north, Tuaregs could travel the desert with ease. Camels could carry heavy loads, withstand heat, and travel long distances on very little water. The caravans moved through the Sahara into West Africa. Tuaregs traded salt for gold, cloth, and European weapons.

Tuaregs raised goats, sheep, and camels. They moved through the desert looking for good pastureland, often conducting raids. Bedouins, unrelated to the Tuaregs, were nomads as well. They migrated from the Middle East to Upper Egypt and finally to the Sahara.

FACT

Assyrian or Persian invaders introduced camels to North Africa around the sixth or seventh century B.C.

Since trees were scarce, nomadic desert groups often used camel dung as cooking fuel. Meat was preserved by soaking it in brine and drying it in the sun. Other staples were camel and goat milk, milk by-products, wild foods, and millet cakes. Dates were eaten fresh or were dried and then soaked in water until plump and ready to eat.

Customs and Beliefs

Religion was an integral part of North African life. Berber beliefs varied among tribes, but many people feared the evil eye. For protection, Berbers developed many rituals and wore safeguarding charms and tattoos.

Christianity was established in the region by the third century A.D. But Arab Islamic influence in the seventh century had a greater impact. Berbers integrated Islam into their customs and beliefs and produced holy men, prophets, saints, and messiahs.

Muslim Berbers, Arabs, and Bedouins prayed five times a day. Prior to their prayers they conducted a ritual cleansing. If water was unavailable, cleansing was performed with sand. Devotees of Islam wore leather pouches around their necks, carrying sayings from the Koran.

The Rise and Fall of Kingdoms

During the first millennium B.C., Phoenician traders established Carthage as a coastal outpost for ships en route to Spain. By A.D. 146, Romans had conquered North Africa. They controlled the land and forced Berbers to pay taxes, most of which were paid with wheat and olive oil. The Romans also wanted gold, acquired through trade with sub-Saharan groups.

The Vandals were a Germanic group who invaded North Africa in A.D. 429 and ousted the deteriorating Roman Empire. In A.D. 643, Arabs started their conquests to convert people to Islam. They introduced Islamic culture, literature, sciences, and written script. They spread Islam into western

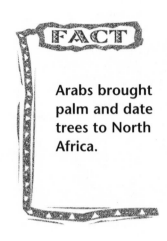

FACT

Arabs brought palm and date trees to North Africa.

Tassili Pictograph

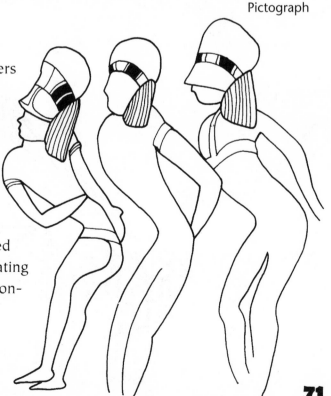

Africa while establishing control over the trade routes of the sub-Saharan caravans.

In 1054 the Almoravid kingdom emerged. For the first time, Berbers were ruled under a single power. The Almoravids were motivated by religious reform. They were disillusioned with Arabs, whom they felt had grown lax in their practices and beliefs. Islamic reformers crossed the Mediterranean Sea to Spain, where the rapid spread of Christianity had threatened Arab Islamic communities. Berber dynasties led to a new Moorish culture in Spain.

The Almoravids dominated Spain and halted the spread of Christianity for more than 30 years. Then another Berber kingdom built on religious reform, the Almohad kingdom, arose in the Atlas Mountains. Almohad leaders saw that the Almoravids had lost their religious fervor. The Almohads led a puritanical crusade that impacted the region for several centuries.

Mediocre rulers, militant tribal divisions, Arab domination, and Islamic-Christian tensions in Spain contributed to the decline of the Almohad Empire. After a period of anarchy, the Merinids established a new kingdom. Merinids were Berbers from the high plains who had fought against the weakened Almohad state for almost 60 years.

The Merinid kingdom faced many difficulties, including threats from the Ottoman Empire. In 1399 the Castilians seized control of most of Spain. Religious fanatics fought to control North African cities. The Portuguese sought to wrest control of the gold trade from Arab middlemen and invaded the Moroccan coast. The Portuguese manipulated various Berber Muslim chieftains from the interior, which caused the last great Berber kingdom to crumble.

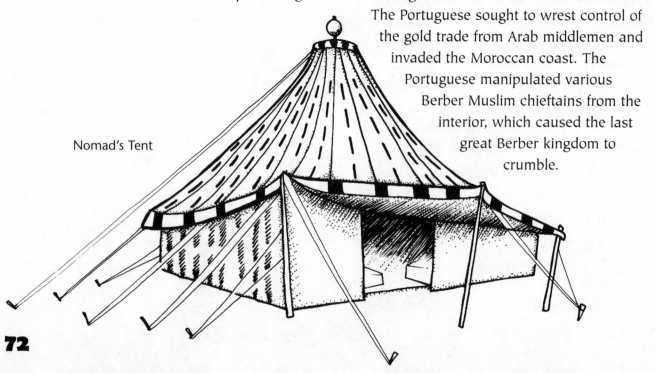

Nomad's Tent

How the Ant Taught the Berbers to Live and Farm

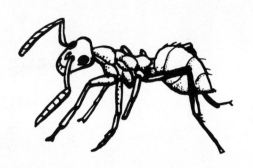

The first man and first woman lived under the earth. One day they stumbled upon large piles of millet, wheat, and barley seeds. Sitting in the middle was an ant who was removing wheat from its husk.

"Kill that ugly creature," the first woman whispered to her husband. "Why should I kill it?" he replied. "Someone created it just as we were created." He crawled next to the ant and asked, "What are you doing? Can you tell me about these seeds?"

The kindly ant obliged. "Do you know the river where one washes his clothes?" he said. "Once the river water is boiled, you may cook the seeds until they're soft enough to eat."

"I know of no such river, nor of cooking and washing," the first man said. "Will you show me?" The ant led the first man and woman through a tunnel to the surface of the earth. "Here is the river," the ant said. "And this is a mill where you can grind your meal." He showed them how to make a fire, knead the bread, and cook a full meal. The first man and first woman were very happy to know these new things.

One day they decided to walk the earth. The first man and first woman took their seeds with them, but some fell to the ground. After a while they turned to go back, and to their surprise they found wheat growing. "This is the same plant that the ant had shown us," they said. Immediately, they threw more seeds upon the earth and waited for them to grow. But the sun burned the fresh stalks to the ground.

The ant saw what had happened. "You have not chosen the right season to grow your grain," he said. "Wait until the rain has fallen. When the earth is damp, throw the seeds out and you will enjoy a rich harvest."

This is why people have always followed what the ant has said.

Group Project

Berber Mini-Rugs

Berber rugs were made of camel hair or wool and were inspired by Arab Islamic designs. Rugs made by the Berbers of the High and Middle Atlas Mountains had geometric and linear designs with monochromatic ochre or red backgrounds. Rugs made in the cities reflected the colors and designs of Moroccan gardens.

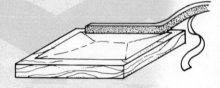

Figure 1

Figure 2

Figure 3

Materials (for each student)

- weather-stripping tape—sponge rubber or plastic foam tape in 1/4-inch (.5-cm) rolls, available in hardware stores
- wood block, 7 x 9 x 1 1/2 inches (17.5 x 22.5 x 3.75 cm)
- acrylic paints: black, white, blue, red, yellow, orange
- brushes in varying sizes   – scissors
- 20 felt rectangles, 8 1/2 x 11 inches (21.25 x 27.5 cm) each
- sturdy muslin cloth, 36 x 57 inches (90 x 142.5 cm)
- carbon paper   – aluminum foil
- white glue   – newspapers

1. Select rug designs from the Berber Designs page or draw designs. Enlarge design on a copier to 7 x 9 inches (17.5 x 22.5 cm).

2. Center and tape enlarged design onto wooden board. Slip carbon paper underneath design and trace lines. Remove design paper and carbon paper.

3. Pull paper backing off weather-stripping tape. Lay sticky side of tape onto wood, following the lines. (Figure 1) This will create a stamp.

4. Spread out 8-x-11-inch (20-x-27.5-cm) sheets of aluminum foil. Tape to table. Spread black paint over aluminum foil. Do *not* let dry. Press stamp into paint. Make sure paint adheres to foam strips.

5. Immediately press wooden block in center of felt rectangle. (Figure 2) Touch up black outlines where the stamp did not produce a solid line.

6. Use other colors to paint inside and outside shapes. Let dry.

7. Repeat stamping process on each felt piece. Glue felt panels onto muslin-cloth backing. Leave a 1-inch (2.5-cm) border on all sides. (Figure 3)

Individual Project

Berber Henna Hand Painting

Berber women used henna for temporary hand designs worn on special occasions. Tuareg Berbers used henna to stain their fingers and toes. Another type of North African body marking was tattooing of hands, feet, and neck. The tattoo designs were geometric and were often inspired by carpet or jewelry motifs. The placement of these tattoos was significant. Tattoos helped establish tribal affiliations, represented magical symbols or charms, and marked rites of passage.

Painting with *harqus* was an alternative to tattooing. Harqus was made from nut galls, ash, spices, charcoal, and oil. It was applied onto the body with a sharp stick called a *calame*.

Before You Begin

The traditional henna hand-painting method offers a dark, rich design. However, the application requires 4 to 5 hours of drying time before scraping henna off the skin. After the henna has been scraped off, it should be kept free of water and remain dry for at least 12 hours. The nontraditional method dyes the skin in less time, but the color is not as intense or long lasting.

Materials for Traditional Henna Painting (for each student)

- 1/8 (30 ml) cup powdered henna, available in many drugstores or beauty supply stores
- eucalyptus oil, available in many health food stores
- 5 tsp. (25 ml) lemon juice
- thin sticks made of wood or plastic
- two small mixing bowls
- 1 tsp. (5 ml) sugar
- small cloth
- mustard oil (traditional) or hand lotion

Materials for Nontraditional Henna Application
(for each student)

- powdered henna
- water
- thin wooden or plastic stick
- mixing bowl

Figure 1

To Paint the Hands

1. Draw around outside of both hands on a sheet of paper. (Figure 1)

2. Choose a design or several designs from the Berber Designs page or draw a design.

3. Draw designs onto hand outlines to use as a model. (Figure 2)

Traditional Method

4. Mix eight drops of eucalyptus oil and two teaspoons (10 ml) of lemon juice in a bowl.

5. Mix henna powder into liquid until it is a wet, sticky lump. Set aside for two hours.

6. Mix rest of lemon juice and sugar in a small bowl. This mixture is used later as you apply the henna.

7. Using designs on model as a guide, apply henna to hands with the small stick. (Figure 3)

8. Make sure the henna on your hands remains moist. Dunk a small cotton cloth into the lemon-sugar water and lightly tap on henna to keep it moist.

9. Scrape henna off after four or five hours. Apply hand lotion or mustard oil. Keep dyed areas dry for at least twelve hours.

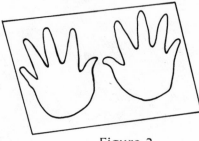

Figure 2

Nontraditional Method

10. Mix a thick paste of henna with tap water.

11. Using designs on model as a guide, apply henna to hands with the small stick. (Figure 3)

12. Once henna dries, flake it off. Keep hands dry for a period of time.

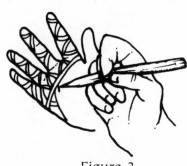

Figure 3

People of North Africa

Berber Designs

These traditional designs were used for Berber rugs and for dyeing hands with henna.

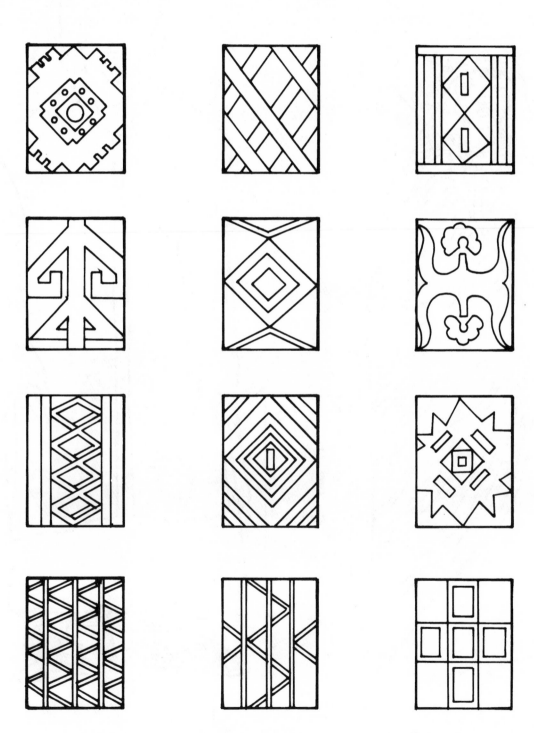

People of North Africa

Garments to Color (Berber)

Color the traditional garments by following the key below.

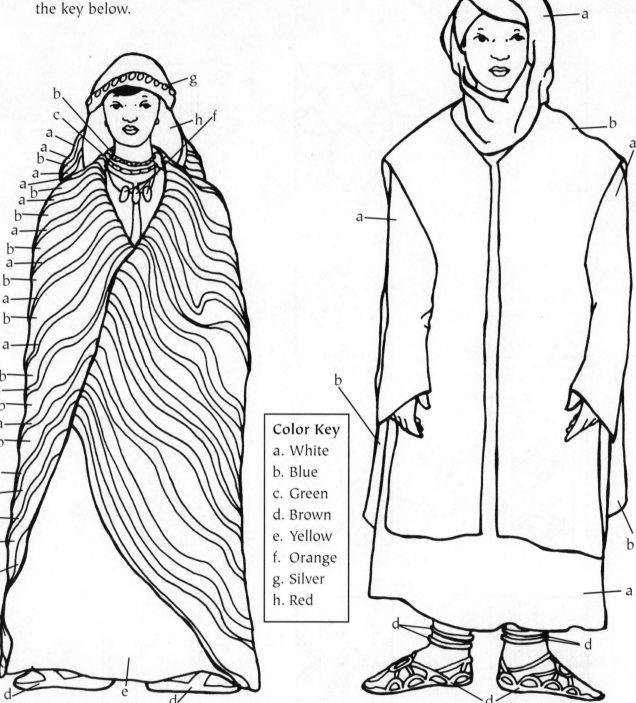

Color Key
a. White
b. Blue
c. Green
d. Brown
e. Yellow
f. Orange
g. Silver
h. Red

(Teacher's note: Use this page as a flat coloring sheet or enlarge each item to use in one of the special projects described on pages 6-7.)

People of North Africa

Tools and Dwellings to Color (Berber)

Color each item by using the color key below.

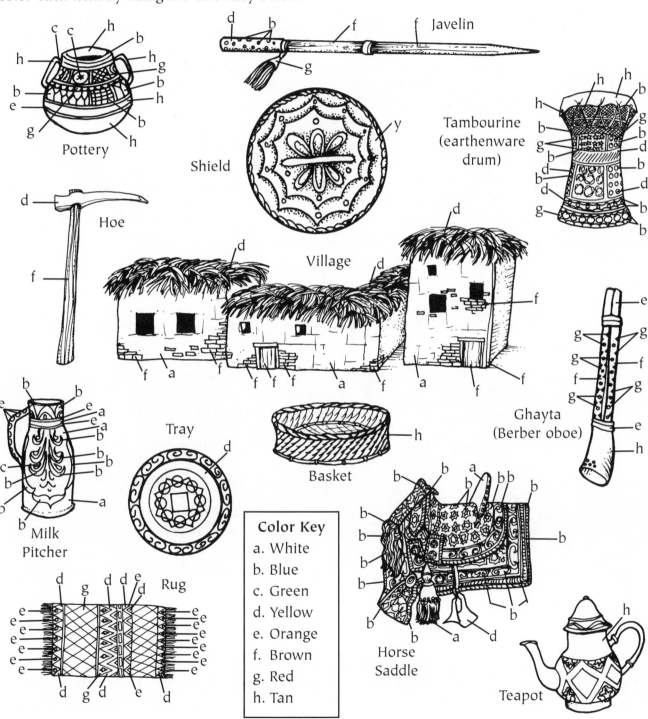

Pottery

Javelin

Shield

Tambourine (earthenware drum)

Hoe

Village

Ghayta (Berber oboe)

Milk Pitcher

Tray

Basket

Color Key
a. White
b. Blue
c. Green
d. Yellow
e. Orange
f. Brown
g. Red
h. Tan

Rug

Horse Saddle

Teapot

(Teacher's note: Use this page as a flat coloring sheet or enlarge each item to use in one of the special projects described on pages 6-7.)

Bibliography

General Reference Books

Africa: Cultural Atlas for Young People by Dr. Jocelyn Murray (Facts on File, 1990).

African Folktales selected and retold by Roger D. Abrahams (Pantheon, 1983).

African Migrations by Dr. Hakim Adi (Thomson Learning, 1994).

Many Thousand Gone: African Americans from Slavery to Freedom by Virginia Hamilton (Knopf, 1992).

Science in Ancient Egypt by Geraldine Woods (Franklin Watts, 1988).

Children's Literature

African Kingdoms of the Past by Kenny Mann (Dillon Press, 1996).

Ashanti to Zulu by Margaret Musgrove (Dial Press, 1976).

Classic African Children's Stories: A Collection of Ancient Tales edited and compiled by Phyllis Savory (Hastings House, 1995).

Her Stories: African American Folktales, Fairy Tales and True Tales by Virginia Hamilton (Blue Sky Press, 1995).

Journey Into Civilization: The Zulus by Robert Nicholson (Chelsea House, 1994).

Kofi and His Magic by Maya Angelou & Margaret Courtney-Clarke (Clarkson N. Potter, 1996).

Kwanzaa: An African Holiday by Sharon Gayle (Watermill Press, 1994).

Mufaro's Beautiful Daughters: An African Tale by John Steptoe (Lothrop, Lee & Shepard, 1987).

Olbalbal: A Day in Maasailand by Barbara A. Margolies (Four Winds Press, 1994).

Our People by Angela Shelf Medearis (Antheneum, 1994).

The Sahara and Its People by Simon Scoones (Thomson Learning, 1993).

Somewhere in Africa by Ingrid Mennen and Niki Daly (Dutton Children's Books, 1990).

The Story of African Flags to Color (Bellerphon Books, 1994).

What Do We Know About the Egyptians? by Joanna Defrates (Peter Bedrick Books, 1991).

The Zulu: Fact, Stories, Activities by Robert Nicholson (Chelsea House, 1994).